the
successful
inventor's guide . . .

the

successful

inventor's guide . . .

... how to develop, protect and sell your invention profitably

k. o. kessler

and

norman carlisle

prentice-hall, inc.
englewood cliffs, n. j.

● this book is dedicated to:

The American Inventor, *whose genius has paced this Nation's Progress.*

and

The Patent Attorney, *whose hard work and unsung contributions smooth the inventor's path.*

Every man who knows how to read has it in his power to magnify himself, to multiply the ways in which he exists, to make his life full, significant and interesting.

—ALDOUS HUXLEY

how and why
this book can help you

Have you just hit on an idea that you believe will make a "million dollar invention"? . . . Are you beyond the idea stage, at the point where you're beginning to think seriously of patents and markets? . . . Perhaps you've already applied for a patent, or have even been granted one . . . Maybe you have developed, patented and sold an invention and are now disappointed with the financial returns. Whatever your situation as an independent inventor, I believe this book will help you.

. . .

Every year, hundreds of inventors write to me, telephone me, or visit my office in Fremont, Ohio. I've never turned anyone away without friendly advice but I sometimes have to give shorter answers than I'd like. That's the reason for this book.

I asked myself: Suppose I could sit with an inventor and pass on to him much that I have learned over my many years of working with inventions? Suppose I could tell my inventor friend that successful inventors—not necessarily clients of mine—had actually succeeded in cashing in on their inventions? Suppose I could impart to him some of the knowledge I've gained in what to do and what not to do? And suppose I could alert him to the booby traps of pricing, production, and marketing; and warn him of the unscrupulous operators who prey on unwary inventors?

Of course, I could not do this for any one inventor. But I *could* set it down in book form. So, with the assistance of Norman Carlisle, the able journalist who has reported the activities of many great inventors, and written many articles on invention subjects for *Popular Science* and other publications, I have presented in these pages the essence of what I would like to tell the independent inventor.

No book, however sound its advice, can perform miracles. There is no possible way in which I or anyone else can tell an inventor how to sell an invention that has no merit. There is no way an inventor can be told how to get more for an invention than it is worth in the marketplace.

But what a book can do, we sincerely believe this one does. We hope that it will go a long way toward helping you find, for your invention, the success it deserves.

k. o. kessler

Fremont, Ohio.

acknowledgments

We acknowledge with gratitude the assistance of many individuals and organizations who contributed to this book:

. . . the *inventors* who told us of their experiences.

. . . the *patent attorneys* who made suggestions; and their professional organization, the Patent Office Society.

. . . the *various government agencies,* especially the U.S. Patent Office, the Small Business Administration, the Department of Commerce, and the Department of Defense.

. . . the *inventor-owned companies and marketing concerns* mentioned in this book.

. . . the *many large manufacturers* which advised us of their policies concerning inventors, especially Aluminum Company of America, Dow Chemical, Du Pont, Eastman Kodak, General Electric, International Business Machines, Minnesota Mining and Manufacturing, Polaroid Corporation, Union Carbide, and Westinghouse.

. . . the *patient librarians* who assisted us at the U.S. Patent Office Library; the Library of Congress; John Crerar Library, Chicago; New York Public Library; and the Engineering Societies Library, N. Y.

. . . and finally, for his valued editorial assistance, we thank *Jon Carlisle.*

contents

13 Selling Your Invention to the U.S. Government—Continued

14 Should You Start Your Own Business?   116

today's independent inventor— american success story

Dr. Robert Horton, a Minnesota physician, had delivered more than a thousand babies. He had often noticed—both in the nursery and at home, where he had three children of his own—that a slow steady noise soothed crying infants. He wondered if there wasn't some particular volume and pitch of sound that was especially comforting. After some experimenting, he found that various "hummers" which gave off sounds in the 320 to 350 cycle per second range proved remarkably effective.

Dr. Horton turned his discovery into an invention—a compact, transistorized humming device, encased in plastic. Powered by two tiny batteries, it can be placed right in a baby's crib. Retailed by department stores all over the country, Dr. Horton's *Slumbertone* has brought him a steady flow of royalties from the hundreds of thousands that have been sold.

. . .

In the little town of Spring Lake, Michigan, James Robbins owned a dry cleaning establishment and a coin-operated laundry. The combination of businesses set him to thinking: Why not invent a coin-operated dry cleaning machine?

To a man with no technical training, the problems involved were awesome. He knew that such a machine, operating without supervision, would have to be foolproof so it wouldn't damage clothes. It would have to be a self-contained unit from which there would be no leakage of volatile cleaning fluids. It would need a highly efficient filter to permit their re-use. And, obviously, it would have to clean clothes for less cost than a conventional dry cleaning establishment had to charge.

Robbins licked all these problems, which had baffled re-rearchers of a number of appliance firms. A major company, Norge, bought rights to his machine and thus sparked a dry cleaning revolution by getting onto the market first with this product dreamed up by an independent inventor. The royalty terms were reportedly such that Robbins was assured of a return of something well over $1,000,000.

. . .

When George Breen retired from selling to live on a Vermont farm, he had no idea that his move was going to make him a successful inventor. Life on the farm was fine, but Breen soon rebelled against the backbreaking work of maple sugaring. Ploughing through the snow to empty the buckets of sap was discouragingly slow.

Breen thought of a better way to do it. Making the discovery that the same pressure that causes the sap to flow would force it through a pipe—even one running uphill—Breen hooked each tree to a system of polyethylene tubing. The sap thereafter flowed directly to the vats.

Breen sought, and got, a patent on his invention, and found an eager buyer for it in the form of the big plastics company which made the tubing. This company, Minnesota Mining and Manufacturing, markets the product under the name of *Mapleflo*. Royalties flow into Breen's pockets at a pleasing rate as his invention is put to work revolutionizing the ancient art of maple sugaring.

. . .

Several hundred technicians from some of America's biggest farm machinery companies gathered, not long ago, on a farm outside Cherokee, Iowa. There they looked with awe, and considerable chagrin, at a marvelous machine. The awe was in response to what the machine did, and how it did it. The chagrin was occasioned by the fact that these same companies had long had teams of researchers at work trying to make such a machine. Years of work and millions of dollars had gone into their unsuccessful efforts.

It was a moment of triumph for the young ex-farmer who watched their reactions, for, as an independent inventor, he had won a race with the teamwork researchers. His machine, a device which squeezes large masses of hay into tine pellets, was now the object of competitive bidding between the different companies whose representatives had come to observe it.

The results of that bidding brought Vernon Lundell—who already had a dozen profitable inventions to his credit—a return that will reportedly run considerably above $2,000,000.

. . .

Years ago a Texan named Edwin Foster watched his wife ironing and got an idea for a safety device. Some kind of a spring mechanism attached to an iron could lift it off the ironing board when the user let go of it. Foster didn't succeed in perfecting the idea at the time—though recently he did, to the joy of the appliance company that makes it—but it got him started on the road to making a fortune from springs.

While struggling to raise a window, he figured there must be an easier way to do it. He invented a spring, consisting of a ribbon of stainless steel, which rolls aluminum windows up and down with ease. It is now used on a large percentage of such windows in the U.S.

When Foster observed a carpenter struggling with a tangled steel rule, he proceeded to develop a spring mechanism that retracted the rule at the push of a button. He further refined his invention so that it made possible longer steel rules than were hitherto considered workable. Foster collects royalties from firms licensed to make these 12-foot or longer rules.

When he saw a gas station attendant tugging at a hose, Foster invented a retracting device that now reels in such hoses. Installed on tens of thousands of gas pumps, it also reels in financial returns for Foster, who is paid a royalty for every one in use.

. . .

It took no more than a few pieces of paper and an idea to create a profitable invention for Beulah Louise Henry, a southern-born New Yorker who is sometimes called the "Lady Edison." With about 40 patents to her credit, she has invented toys, household appliances, and novelty items, many of which have earned her upwards of $10,000.

What Miss Henry created with the pieces of paper was a remarkable envelope, designed to be used by companies which send out many bills. The recipient tears off a flap, takes out his statement, inserts a check, pulls out another flap, and then seals the envelope, which is now all ready to mail back to the company. Because of the way the envelope is made it can be manufactured in continuous strips, stuffed, and addressed by machine.

Big paper companies and office machine makers had never come up with this simple, effective design, and Miss Henry was rewarded for her ingenuity with a patent—and a starting order from a utility company for 70,000,000 of these products of her inventive paper work.

. . .

Once he got his idea for a needed invention, Ross Williams had to go no farther than the corner drug store for the makings. What travelers needed, he thought, was a way to wash without water. In the kitchen of his New York apartment, he and his wife tried impregnating paper towels with various lotions. It took a lot of experimenting before they found a combination that worked.

Williams was able to get the $250,000 he had to have to go into the business of making his invention. The company he set up sold $1,000,000 worth of the product, the now famous *Wash 'n Dri*, the first year.

. . .

A broken leg led to the successful invention of Nat Cabot, a New York advertising man who is also an ardent golfer. He was convalescing at home, grumbling about the fact that he wouldn't get onto the golf links for weeks. His game was going to suffer plenty—unless he could figure out some way to practice his swings at home.

With a lot of time to think about that, Cabot hit on the idea of a tethered ball. Hobbling around, he started tinkering, quickly discovering that the main problem was fastening a cord to a standard golf ball. Cabot experimented with 40 different ways of doing it before he at last developed a special pin that accomplished what he wanted—a ball that would be as controllable with the pin in it as it would be without.

The way fellow golfers took to the device told Cabot he had an invention that could make money—and it did. Since its main components are a golf ball, a metal pin, a wooden block to which the ball is tethered, and a 30-foot cord of resilient synthetic fiber, manufacturing is simple. Cabot set up his own company to make *Returno-Golf*. Sold in hundreds of sporting goods stores all over the country, it raises Cabot's bank account as it lowers the scores of the golfers who use it to "turn a backyard into a fairway."

These success stories of today's independent inventors are not isolated instances. They are just a few of the hundreds the authors have encountered in our roles as science reporter and invention broker. Every one of them is matched by stories of equal or greater success in the fields they represent. Not many inventors, to be sure, do have what turns out to be a "million dollar invention," but many have come up with inventions which make them between $10,000 and $50,000.

In fact, so many ingenious Americans, from all walks of life, are profiting from their inventions, that we venture to make what may seem a startling statement in an age when so many new developments are produced by team work researchers in big labs.

We believe that *never before has the opportunity for the independent inventor been so great.*

Here, as we see them, are five big factors that favor your success as an independent inventor today:

• 1 • Your whole inventing process has been made easier by the products turned out by the big laboratories. Plastics, alloys, light metals, ceramics, synthetic fibers, super glues, chemical treatments for wood, paper and cloth—these and other products of modern technology give you a running start. In many cases, your invention has been partly invented for you. Dr. Horton, for instance, did not need to invent the miniature batteries, the transistors, nor the sturdy plastic housing for his *Slumbertone.* Nat Cabot was able to take his choice of dozens of synthetic fibers for his tether cord.

• 2 • The 1952 Amendment to the Patent Law enables you to gain patent protection for inventions which utilize such "combinations." It states, "Whoever invents or discovers any new and useful process, machine, manufacture, or composition of matter, or any new and useful improvement thereof, may obtain a patent therefor." Moreover, the word "process" is spelled out to include a "new use of a known process."

• 3 • There is a vast and growing consumer market for small, simple gadgets of the type which the independent inventor can easily dream up and develop. The booming market in recreational equipment alone seems capable of absorbing an almost indefinite number of innovations. The do-it-yourself boom and the countless special needs of suburbanites, with their lawns, gardens, patios and home improvement efforts, have provided another sweeping market for independent inventors.

• 4 • More companies than ever before are buying "outside inventions." Even big corporations, many of which formerly cold shouldered independent inventors, now consider their offerings. General Electric, IBM, Westinghouse, DuPont, and Minnesota Mining and Manufacturing are just a few of the big firms which have recently purchased such inventions. While such concerns, with research set-ups of their own, are not, statistically, a large market for inventions, their interest in the products of the independents is significant.

Of more importance to you is the fact that so many small firms, with machinery they want to keep operating and sales organizations they want to keep busy, are eagerly seeking new items to manufacture and sell. These companies, with limited research and development facilities of their own, find the independent inventor an important source of money-making new products.

• 5 • If you choose to set up your own company to make and sell your invention, the problem of financing it has never been easier than it is today. Peter Hilton, noted authority on merchandising innovations, says, "The atmosphere today is ripe for attracting money for interesting new products." (*Handbook of New Product Development*—Prentice-Hall, 1961.)

An amendment to the Small Business Administration's investment law makes sources of local capital available. Numerous inventors have found it possible to raise $10,000 to $250,000 (as did Ross Williams) to get their inventions into production.

protecting your invention
starts at home

Invention protection begins the moment you get your idea. There are certain simple steps that should be initiated before you know whether you have a patentable invention, before you know whether your invention will work, before you have fully developed it.

Because they don't know they should take these steps or are reluctant to take them, many inventors have lost inventions that may have been rightfully theirs.

Neither of these vital steps costs any money, beyond a few dollars for notary fees. Neither requires going outside your home or place of work. However, they do require jumping a mental hurdle difficult for many inventors. To take two of them you must rid your mind of the unreasonable fear that somebody is going to try to steal your invention.

● the need for records and witnesses

What you are guarding against right from the start is being on the losing end of an "interference." This is the Patent Office term for the situation that arises when it finds itself considering the applications of two inventors who appear to be making the same claims for their inventions. In that case, the problem of the Patent Office is to decide, not who filed his application first, but who actually conceived of the invention and "reduced it to practice" first.

(For a full discussion of the subject of interference cases, see Chapter 9, *Getting Your Patent.*)

Suppose that after you get your idea you plug away for six months before you get your invention to work. You then file an application for a patent. But suppose that, four months after you got your idea, someone, somewhere, perhaps across the continent, perhaps in the next block, gets the same idea. And suppose he jumps the gun, doesn't bother to reduce his invention to practice—that is, make a model and really get it working—and actually files his application ahead of yours. *You* are the first inventor, but how are you going to prove it?

With two kinds of evidence: *records* and *witnesses*. They must reveal the exact date when two events occurred: (1) The date when you conceived of the invention, and (2) the date when you reduced it to practice.

Look briefly at the ground rules covering these points before we examine the ways of building up the evidence you may need. First let us explain that there are two kinds of reduction to practice—*actual* and *constructive*. Actual reduction to practice is the building of a functioning model that successfully embodies the inventive concept. Constructive reduction to practice is putting the invention on paper, and describing it in a fashion that insures the successful operation of the invention, if built as described. In most cases the date of constructive reduction to practice is the date of the patent application.

If you were the first inventor to conceive the invention and also the first to reduce it to practice, you win the interference.

You also win if you were the first to conceive and the second to reduce, if you can prove what is called diligence. Diligence means what it sounds like—a more or less consistent effort to reduce the invention to practice. This doesn't mean you must have spent every hour of every day doing it. The courts have held that consistent spare-hours' work constitutes diligence.

But if you were the second to reduce, you are therefore the junior party, and must have very good proof of your prior date of conception and your diligence. This proof must be in the form of proper records and witnesses' testimony. If you cannot *prove* your prior conception *and* your diligence, you will lose the interference.

If you were the second to conceive but the first to reduce, you can do everything in your power to challenge the other party's diligence. In such a case, he may try to prove an earlier date of constructive reduction to practice than that of his patent application. Your attorney can challenge this proof and even attempt to show the records are not straight or question the veracity of your opponent's witnesses, just as his attorney can challange yours.

That is why you must make sure that both your records and your witnesses are beyond reproach. You start with the records. Ideally, you begin them the day you get your idea. Of course, you don't know whether this idea is really going to develop into an invention, but just in case it does, you'd be smart to give it a proper start in life.

● the documentary evidence

The records you keep are the foundation of your proof of what you invented and when. The heart of your records is your notebook, in which you describe in detail, as you go along, each step you make toward development of your invention.

The notebook should be a bound one; a looseleaf one won't do. When you buy it, be sure you get a sales slip for it, plainly dated. You might paste this sales slip into the front of the notebook. You may also do well to have the first page of the notebook notarized, having the notary's seal placed on the first page.

At the time you buy your notebook, start a file of sales slips covering each and every piece of apparatus you purchase for the development of your invention. Be sure that they are itemized and dated. There is no need to have such sales slips notarized.

There are certain definite rules you should follow in making your entries in the notebook. Basically, you are going to tell (1) what you did, (2) why you did it, (3) when you did it, (4) why what you did was significant.

In general, your entries should be clearly stated, so that "any person skilled in the art" can understand them. You should not do what some inventors have done and write them in code. Even though you later present a key to your code, *the examiners will disallow code-written notes* in an interference case. You should keep your records up to date. Better to put down briefly, "Today I worked on the proper placement of the valve sleeve," than to put down nothing at all.

When you make a mistake, do not erase. The proper way to handle an error is to draw a line through the erroneous words and write the proper ones above the crossed-out ones. If, at some later date, you read over your records and have some fresh thoughts about something you have written, don't make changes. Instead, make new notes at the time you have such second thoughts.

Do not hesitate to put down your failures as you go. The things that didn't work, the false trials you went down, the schemes that came to nothing, are all part of the running record of your invention. They help prove your "diligence" in "reducing to practice" what started out as just an idea.

State in your record your line of reasoning and the sources of your information. Tell *exactly* what ingredients, parts, or equipment you used.

This detailed information may afterwards become a part of your patent application, as it did in the case of Mike Remeika, a Madison, Wisconsin, inventor who developed a corn cob pipe which blows bubbles upon immersion in water. Here is his explicit description of one way he found to give the pipe its special properties.

"The bowl of a corn cob pipe was placed in a glass container and boiling water poured over it. The bowl was then removed and immersed for approximately 12 hours in a heated solution comprising one part by weight of glycerine and two parts by weight of a detergent having the following composition:

"Composition: Parts by weight
Methyl alcohol 20
Kyro EO (alkyl phenol-ethylene oxide condensate
    produced by Procter & Gamble Co.) 20
Solar CO (a coconut oil-fatty acid condensate
    produced by Swift & Co.) 5
Ultrawet 35 KX (an alkyl benzene sodium sul-
    fonate produced by Atlantic Refining Co.) 10
Ultrawet 60 L (alkyl benzene sulfonate of organic
    salt produced by Atlantic Refining Co.) 5
Armid C (a high molecular weight aliphatic amide
    having an alkyl chain length of from 8–18 car-
    bon atoms and derived from coco fatty acids
    produced by Armour Chemical Co.) 1

"The bowl was then removed from the solution and allowed to dry. The inside surface of the bowl was then scraped to remove any rough surfaces or loose particles therein. The stem of the pipe was then inserted into the bowl to provide a bubble pipe."

● the witnesses you need

Your records, no matter how carefully kept, are not enough to prove you're really the inventor if the matter comes to an inter-ference—a fate that befalls about one patent application in fifty. You must have at least two credible, legally acceptable witnesses who have *observed and understood the nature of your invention.*

This last requirement is the stumbling block to many inventors haunted by the fear that if they really tell all to a witness, the witness will either run off with the invention himself or talk indiscreetly and reveal details to some scoundrel who, having been given the idea, will promptly file for a patent.

There is absolutely nothing to either fear. That's the unanimous opinion of anyone in the business we've ever talked to. For one thing, you can choose your witnesses on the basis of their known integrity. They don't necessarily need to be experts in the field, though if they are technical-minded that can be helpful, perhaps making it easier to prove that they understood what you told them. However, acceptable witnesses often have no technical background at all. The main point here is that it is up to you to fill in the gaps in the witnesses' knowledge.

We must caution you that one person you cannot use as a witness is your wife—or husband. The courts have long held that the testimony of a mate would be like the inventor's own testimony in his favor. This goes for other relatives, too. In one court case in which the question hinged on the inventor's diligence in pursuing his invention, his only witness was his brother-in-law, whose testimony was disallowed.

What is a witness expected to witness? As many points of progress on your invention as possible. When you first get the idea, or as near to that time as possible, you'd do well to describe the nature of your invention to your witnesses and show them any drawings you have made. These, of course, will be based on the items in your notebooks. You can have them initial and date the drawings, and either sign a letter or initial a statement which describes what you have told them. The drawings and the letter or statement should then be notarized.

As you move forward on your invention, making various

breakthroughs in its development, you should explain them and have them witnessed and notarized. Don't let there be any long gaps between these "progress reports." Remember that one of the requirements for establishing your claims as the inventor of a particular device is diligence.

When you demonstrate and explain your invention to the witnesses, don't make the mistake of just showing them what it does. Show them *how* it does it. The testimony of many witnesses has been disallowed because the inventor failed to prove to them just how something was accomplished. That was what happened in the case of a pitch pipe, the inventor of which merely told his witnesses it used an electrostatic condenser. He did not show them the condenser, but only the finished product in which it was embodied.

Another case of disallowed testimony involved a new golf ball. The inventor demostrated the ball in action, but did not show its interior construction. In still another case, this rule was applied to a door lock.

While these witnesses had been shown evidence that certain inventions really worked, the inventors had not demonstrated the means by which they worked. Follow the general rule that the·more you show your witnesses, and the more fully you explain everything to them, the better off you'll be if their testimony is ever needed.

can you patent
your invention?

You have an invention. Or perhaps simply an idea for an invention.

What do you do with it? How do you protect it, develop it, and turn it into the money maker you think it can be? Where do you start?

You start by seeking the answer to the number one question that confronts all inventors, wherther they work for big research laboratories or in basement workshops: *Can you patent it?*

● what is a patent?

To get the full answer as to what you can—and can't— patent, let's begin at the beginning. What is a patent?

A *patent*, as defined by the Patent Office itself, is "a grant by the United States to an inventor of the right to exclude others for a limited time from making, using, or selling his invention in this country. It is a printed document in which the invention is fully disclosed and the rights of the inventor are defined. When an inventor secures a patent he has the opportunity to profit by manufacture, sale, or use of the invention in a protected market, or by charging others for making or using it. In patents granted for inventions of new processes, machines, manufactures, compositions of matter or plants, the patent rights run for 17 years from the date when the patent is granted. A patent for an ornamental design for an article of manufacture may run for 3½, 7, or 14 years, as desired by the patentee."

The Patent Office goes on to say that these privileges are not granted to you to enable you to profit from your invention. On the contrary, they are granted for the *public* benefit. By offering patent protection, the government stimulates invention and thereby helps get new and worthwhile items into public use. Also the filing of patents creates a running record of technological progress, a treasure trove of knowledge for scientists, engineers and researchers, as well as for other inventors.

So if some of the procedures involved in getting a patent, or the requirements your invention must meet to qualify for one, seem unreasonable to you, remember that the Patent Office is not set up for the purpose of helping you make money. As befits a public agency, it is working primarily for the public good.

If you're thinking of applying for a patent, you should start by considering what might keep you from getting one. Of course, the one reason everybody knows is that you can't patent anything that has ever been patented before. Not so well known perhaps is the fact that this means *patented anywhere in the world*. (See Chapter 4 for a complete discussion of just how you find out if a particular invention has been patented.)

But there are other reasons, too, why you can be denied a patent. It can save you time, trouble and the pursuit of false hopes if you check your invention against the list of factors that can make it unpatentable.

● what can't you patent?

You cannot patent your invention if you have had a description (pictorial or verbal) published in any book, magazine, newspaper, film, or any other place of public record more than 𝕀 a year prior to the filing of your application. In such a case, the invention would already be in the public domain. Of course, nobody else can get a patent on your invention either, if you are the first inventor.

You cannot patent your invention if it has been in public use or on public display or offered to the public for sale more than a year prior to application. The reasons for this are much the same as those for the last point.

You cannot patent your invention if it won't work. In other words, you can't get a patent on a useless invention, such as a machine that has three gears in it, each of which mesh with the other two at all times, thereby freezing all of them and rendering the machine inoperative. (Not that you would want to!)

This brings up an important point. The Patent Office makes no exhaustive test as to whether your invention works or not, in most cases. If what you say you're invented is not contrary to known laws of mechanics, chemistry or physics, they take your word that it does what you say it does. Therefore, patents are granted on inventions that don't work. But those patents are ruled invalid if the question of workability comes up.

The Patent Office once issued a patent to an inventor on a voting machine. Another inventor later sought a patent on a machine that was substantially the same, claiming the first machine didn't work. The case went to court, where is was found that the first machine worked with 99% accuracy; the second with 100%. In the decision of the court, a voting machine did not work unless it was absolutely accurate. It was ruled that the first machine did not work for the purpose for which it was intended, and that the patent was invalid. The second man got his patent. He was "the first inventor" because he was the first to make the invention work.

You cannot patent anything you did not invent. Probably every patent attorney in the country (certainly every one we've talked to) has had people come to him trying to patent the inventions of others, evidently thinking that the first person to make an application is the one who gets the patent. This is definitely not so. Neither can you hire someone to invent something for you and claim yourself as the inventor. You must be the "true," "sole" and "only" inventor to get a patent.

You cannot patent your invention if it really isn't an invention, but is just an idea. The notion that you can is one of the most widespread of all invention fallacies. Patent attorneys are continually beset by people who come to them with the announcement, "I've got an idea I want to patent."

A conversation may go something like this:

"I've got an invention—a refrigerated hat."

"How does it work?"

"Well, some kind of refrigerant . . . maybe a battery operated cooling unit. . . . I don't know exactly, but anyway I want to protect the idea."

At this point the attorney must wearily explain that a patent can be granted only on a definite, workable structure or process that will accomplish the desire purpose—in this case cooling a hat.

Lastly, you cannot get a patent on anything that is "obvious to people in the art."

"The art" means the particular technological or commercial area in which a given invention can be classed. That an invention must not be obvious simply means that you cannot get a patent if the ordinary person skilled or knowledgeable in "the art" could have done just what you did with limited work or thought. Here again it's a question of public benefit, which would not gain, and might suffer, if you were to be granted an exclusive license to exploit some structure or process that isn't really advanced over what is known as "the present state of the art."

The 1952 amendment to the Patent Law, which allows the patentability of "a new use of a known process" provides a clear-cut answer to a question which has plagued inventors, lawyers, and courts for years. What is a patentable combination of parts and what is not?

The whole sticky question involved such classic cases as one of the last century in which the court said that a patent granted to an inventor on a combination hoe and rake (hoe facing one way, rake the other) was invalid. The reason? Basically what the court decided was that the hoe was still a hoe and the rake still a rake and that therefore this "invention" was not new.

Years later, in another similar case, the court decided that putting an eraser on the end of a pencil did not constitute invention. The eraser still erased and the pencil still wrote; neither did anything more in combination than they did separately. However, patents *were* granted for specific *means* whereby a pencil and an eraser could be hooked together.

Now the inventor has been given more room. Obviously, it is easier to get a patent on a combination of parts under a law stating specifically that "a new use of a known process" is patentable.

Witness how this has worked out for one successful "combination" invention:

Michael Meyerberg, a New York theatrical producer, thought American women needed a better light by which to put on their make-up. He had never seen, even in the theater, where make-up was of such importance, what he considered a properly lighted make-up mirror. Fluorescent lights around a mirror didn't provide enought light or distribute it right. Neither did low wattage incandescents. Yet incandescent lamps of high wattage were too hot.

When Meyerberg got in touch with engineers at General Electric, he found they had the answer to his problem—a cool 15-watt lamp with a special frosting inside that gave a strong, diffused light.

He rigged up a compact, three-part mirror that could be used both in the theater and at home, mounting five of the lamps on each post and four above the center mirror. That was all there was to it. His invention was simply a mirror and GE's already patented light bulbs, yet it qualified for, and got, a patent for Meyerberg.

So far we've been talking about mechanical patents, the kind by which most inventions are best protected. However, there are two other kinds.

● you can patent a design

A design patent, as its name indicates, is a patent granted on the way something looks. In other words, if you have come up with a new design for some article of manufacture, it is possible that you can protect your rights to your design with a patent. A design patent thus obtained gives you the right to exclude others from making, using or selling objects that are protected by it.

There are three major qualifications your design must have to be patentable. **It must be new.** No other design patent can describe an identical design or one different only in very minor details. **Secondly, it must be pleasing.** (Judging by some design patents that have been issued, apparently it's enough if it pleases only one individual—the inventor.) **Lastly, the design as patented must be visible on the eventual item of manufacture** when the item is in use.

You could, for instance, get a patent on some particular ornamentation—a design in colored checkerboard pattern, let's say—for the walls of automobile tires, but you could not get a patent for a new tread design. Such patents have been disallowed on the grounds that a tire tread cannot be considered "pleasing" to the eye because it really isn't there to be looked at. It has a purely utilitarian function.

Similarly, you cannot get a design patent on the appearance of some part of a machine that is buried inside the machine where nobody can see it, no matter how beautiful its shape. This bar to design patentability is known in the patent business as the "doctrine of obscure use," and we're sure that you can readily see many of its implications.

There are some designs on which you can't get a patent. You cannot patent any literal rendition of objects of nature for purposes of external ornamentation. Nor can you patent a "moving" design. That is, to be patentable, your design must not have any moving parts. If it did, the appearance of the article could not always be the same as that delineated in your patent claim.

Design patents have covered the appearance of whole buildings, including churches, skyscrapers, factories, grandstands and homes. They cover the external, visual aspects of machines, including automobiles, road graders and industrial equipment.

And of course there are the thousands of design patents granted for such items as household effects, clothing, jewelry, toys, novelties, combs, and so on down almost the entire list of consumer goods. A design patent may be important on any article of manufacture which depends on its "look" for its sale.

A design patent and a mechanical patent will not be issued on the same material. You can, of course, patent the mechanics of your invention under a mechanical patent and the external appearance under a design patent. But if the mechanics of your invention are inseparable from its appearance, you have to patent one way or the other, not both.

● you can patent a plant

Before 1930 there was no such thing as a plant patent. With the thought that if plant breeders were offered patent protection for any new varieties of plants they developed, new and useful plants might come into existence, the patent law was amended to allow the granting of patents on new plants.

Plant patents are granted to anyone "who has invented or discovered and asexually reproduced any distinct and new variety of plant, including cultivated sports, mutants, hybrids, and newly found seedings, other than a tuber-propagated plant or a plant found in an uncultivated state."

Basically what a plant patent gives the inventor is the right to stop others from asexually producing his new plant—as by grafting—but not from sexually reproducing it, with seeds.

4

preliminary search:
key to patentability

Has somebody already invented **your** invention?

Is there, somewhere, a device or process that exactly duplicates that ingenious, and, as far as you're concerned, completely original, brainchild of yours?

You can't know for sure until you've gone through the whole process of applying for a patent and waiting for the Patent Office examiners to make their search of the more than 3,000,000 U.S. patents, the more than 6,000,000 foreign ones, and the mass of technical literature assembled in the Patent Office's vast library in Washington.

On a mechanical patent it can take as long as three years (design patents come through much faster) to get the final answer. Fortunately, there is a way to get a tentative answer, and get it in a matter of days or weeks.

We're talking about the preliminary search. It is not done for you by the Patent Office. You hire it done, or do it yourself, and you go through no red tape, no delay whatsoever, to get it underway. You need no contact with the Patent Office, no official permission or document.

● what is a search?

A preliminary search, as it is usually carried out, consists of checking through all U.S. patents to see if any of them conflict

23

with a particular invention. In some cases a preliminary search is extended to include a check of foreign patents, but this is rarely considered to be worth the added effort and expense.

The search is usually made by a professional searcher, working in the Search Room in the Patent Office in Washington. (This part of the Patent Office is public and can be used by anyone.)

The searcher starts his work by consulting the *Manual of Classification*, a looseleaf index. In it are listed the groups into which the Patent Office has classified U.S. patents.

If you have hired a searcher, he will ascertain the numbers of the classes and subclasses which he considers pertinent to your invention, and obtain the folders containing the patents in these categories. He'll look at every patent carefully, checking it against your invention.

If he finds a patent which covers substantially the same thing as what you think you've invented, the searcher's job is over. You can't get a patent. In the jargon of the trade, you have been "anticipated."

Maybe the searcher finds two or more patents, each of which covers a part of your invention. A good searcher will find such patents, if they exist, and if the relationship between them and your invention is at all close. If all parts of your invention have been anticipated in various patents, you are just as unlucky as if there had been a single blanketing patent.

The searcher will send you copies of all patents on which he has based his judgment. He will do more than that for you, however. If he finds that there are features in your invention that have not been patented, he will tell you which parts, and indicate the possibility of obtaining a patent on these particular innovations. It's up to you to decide whether these limited features have sufficient commercial value to warrant the expense of seeking a patent on them.

Of course, if the search uncovers no patents that anticipate your invention, either in whole or in part, you have a green light on trying for a patent.

● when should the search be made?

At what stage of your idea-to-invention process should the search be made? Should you have it done early in the day, when your invention is still formative? Should you wait until you've licked all the problems and really have a workable invention?

There are some arguments on both sides. Most professional inventors we have observed tend to search early. One very successful one, with more than 50 patents to his credit, orders a search, as he puts it, "at the drop of an idea." Such early search advocates argue that: (1) It's better to find out fast if you really have an original idea; the chances are good that, no matter how fresh you think it is, there are already competing patents. (2) Seeing how the other fellow did it may sharpen your thinking and help you in "reducing to practice." You'll be able to see more clearly wherein your concept is superior. (3) It may reveal a crowded field and indicate that your invention might be difficult to market. If you find a lot of patents for devices similar to yours, and yet have never seen them on the market, you should take warning.

Late search proponents hold that it's better to have your invention fully thought through and developed, otherwise you can't really give your searcher an adequate idea of what he's looking for. General similarities of inventions aren't too meaningful; many patents are granted on the basis of one or two really novel claims.

You'll have to fit the timing of the search to your individual needs, but if your invention really requires a great amount of development work you'll be wise to take early steps to make sure you're not just duplicating something somebody else patented, perhaps long ago.

Many professional inventors find it a profitable investment to have two searches made—one early and one late, as a tighter check against the exact details of an invention as it is finally perfected.

● how to find a searcher

If you want to hire a search made, the best procedure is to contact a patent attorney or agent. (See Chapter 7.) A list of all such registered practitioners is published by the Patent Office. You can buy it for $1 from the Supt. of Documents, U.S. Government Printing Office, Washington, D.C. Or you can look at it in any field office of the U.S. Dept. of Commerce or the Small Business Administration (see the *Reference Guide* for complete listing of these offices), or at any public library which is a depository of government publications.

Also, the Patent Office will send you a list of attorneys and agents in your region of the country. This is free, and you can get it by writing to the Commissioner of Patents, Patent Office, U.S. Department of Commerce, Washington, D.C.

Many attorneys and agents do their own searching. Others work with professional searchers whom they trust to do a thorough job. It is obviously advantageous to have a searcher with a wide background of knowledge in the particular field of your invention. A searcher who is top-flight in one field may be less competent in another. The patent attorney or agent knows which searcher (if not himself) will be best qualified to search your invention.

● what to tell your searcher

The professional searcher always has an extensive technical education; many have engineering degrees. So you need not be afraid your invention will be over the searcher's head. Since he can't do anything unless he does understand your invention, make your description and drawings clear, explicit, and as simple as possible without leaving out any essentials. It is not necessary to have a professional draftsman make your drawings if you can do it well enough to make your invention clearly understood in all its parts.

Don't leave out some important feature of your invention because you're afraid the searcher will "steal" it. He won't. There's not a single case on record of any such theft ever having been made. The searcher, of all people, is keenly aware of the law which makes it a federal offense to claim you are the inventor of something you did not in fact invent. Moreover, you are protected by numerous other aspects of the law— as your attorney can explain to you.

You must give your searcher as much data as you can about what your invention is supposed to do and how it does it, so that he can quickly narrow the field of search. The faster he can do the job, the less money it will cost you.

● what does a search cost?

A preliminary search has a general price tag of $35 to $50. Of course, in the case of a very complicated invention, it might cost far more. When you order a search you don't have to buy a pig in a poke. You can expect your searcher to give you a very close estimate as to cost. He is able to judge probable costs because of his previous experience in making similar searches.

Perhaps you've seen advertisements offering searches at bargain prices of less than $10. We advise you to beware of them. A proper search can hardly be made for such prices. It's axiomatic that *a poor search is worse than no search.*

If it misses patents that anticipate your invention, it could encourage you to go ahead and seek a patent which you have no chance of getting. On the other hand, if the cut-rate searcher fails to analyze the really original claims in your invention correctly, the faulty search could keep you from seeking a patent which you might get. Either way you lose.

Actually, the greatest danger is that such a low cost searcher will make no real search at all. He'll simply write back to tell you the glad tidings: He found no patent that conflicts with yours; you should go ahead and apply for a patent—of course, hiring him to prepare the application for you. (For a full discussion of added dangers in engaging such a person, see Chapter 7.)

● can you make your own search?

Can you cut out any search fees by conducting your own search? Yes, you can, and there are a number of ways of going about it. But before we discuss them we want to issue a warning to the effect of "proceed at your own risk." You may be a genius at inventing, but the question of whether you have the peculiar blend of ability, patience and know-how essential to a good patent searcher is something quite different.

It's all too easy to slip up in the exacting business of analyzing patent claims. We've known of cases in which do-it-yourself searchers learned too late that they had incorrectly decided their inventions were unpatentable. We've also heard of the reverse situation in which faulty self-searches have led to futile patent applications.

One inventor we know—a top professional with more than 50 patents to his credit—swears by the value of making his own searches. Another, a man who has made $4,000,000 from his 15 inventions, confesses that he tried it and gave up in dismay. Both are engineers highly competent in their fields.

Maybe you're the exception to the rule, the inventor who can make his own search successfully. So if you think you are, here's how to go about it.

• making your own search in the patent office

In Washington, you can use the Search Room at the Patent Office, which is in the Department of Commerce Building, 14th and E Streets, N.W. It's public and you may work there as long as you like, from 8:30 AM to 9 PM every weekday, and from 8:30 to half past noon on Saturdays.

Attendants are always on duty to help you. Explain to one of them what you are looking for and he will consult the *Manual of Classification* with you to find what classes and subclasses of patents are pertinent to your invention. Then he will point out the place in the stacks where you will find the patent bundles you will need to go through.

Then you start looking. You don't just glance at the drawings to see if you come across one that looks like your invention. You look at every patent long enough to find out whether it's relevant. If you find any that are, read them carefully all the way through, including the paragraphs at the end which follow the inventor's words "I claim:"

It's the claims which you must read with most care, for they define precisely what a patent covers. Each word in them is there for a specific purpose. Conversely, anything not said is not said for just as specific a reason. You've got to understand the claims of a patent to know whether it covers your invention. It may take several readings before you get the hang of them, and a lot of hard mental exertion to decide whether or not you've been beaten to the patent.

After you go through the patents closely related to your invention, you should branch out (as a good professional searcher does) into related areas. You may find some essential part of your invention included in the patent on a second cousin of your invention.

When you're finished with your study of the patents, you should buy those you think are most important to you, so that you can study them at your leisure. The cost is 25¢ apiece on mechanical patents, 10¢ on design patents.

● patent searching in local libraries

Bound volumes containing the patents in numerical order—that is, arranged according to the dates on which they were issued—are to be found in the public libraries of some 20 major cities. (See complete list of these libraries in the *Reference Guide.*) These libraries also have the numbers of the patents appearing in the various classifications and sub-classifications. However, they do not have packets of patents arranged by classification.

We warn you, therefore, that while it is possible to do a search in these libraries, it is a cumbersome procedure, compared with that which you follow in Washington, where the patents are available by classification. Thus, if a sub-class in which you are looking for relevant patents contains, say, 80 patents, you may find, in your local library, that they are scattered through as many volumes. Lugging that many heavy books to a desk can be both exhausting and exasperating. Moreover, it's highly unlikely that you can confine your search to one sub-class.

You may be able to lighten your task somewhat by looking up the patents in the *Patent Gazette,* which your library may have. The *Gazette* prints abbreviated forms of all patents, and reproduces certain drawings. A quick glance at these drawings and short accounts may tell you that a particular invention is nothing like yours. However, if there should be the slightest similarity, you can't rely on the *Patent Gazette* to tell you whether there is real conflict with your invention. You must, as we've said, examine the claims in minute detail, and the claims, unfortunately, are omitted in the *Gazette.*

However, don't let us discourage you. If you can't do the job in Washington, and are not ready to hire a searcher, and are possessed of great patience, you can do a search in one of the libraries that has the numbered patents.

● how to make a search by mail

Here is still another way of making your own search. Write a letter to the Commissioner of Patents, Patent Office, U.S. Department of Commerce, Washington, D.C. 20025. Describe what you've invented and ask him to "define the proper field of search."

You will get back a letter listing the classes and/or sub-classes of patents which, in the opinion of the Patent Office, are thought to be most relevant to your invention. This opinion is in no way official. You cannot hold the Patent Office responsible if you are later denied a patent on the basis of some patent or patents in a sub-class not mentioned in the list sent you.

If you choose this method, be sure you make your initial letter specific. Put into it a description of how your invention is constructed, how it works, and what it's used for—much the same thing you'd send a searcher, up to and including the drawings, if you have them.

If you aren't specific, the Patent Office will have no other choice than to send you a long list of patent classifications—most of which will probably be of no importance to you. Thus, if you have invented, let's say, a small, portable, gas-burning stove for use by campers and picnickers, which has what you think is a new, improved burner arrangement and control system—that's what you say. Don't just say you have invented a stove, or you'll get a list of patent classifications that pertain to electric kitchen ranges, gas kitchen ranges, woodburning stoves, etc.

When you have this list of classifications, you write another letter to the Commissioner and ask for a list of the patent numbers in the classifications he has mentioned. You also ask how many "listing sheets" it will take to list them. Each sheet is big enough for 100 patent numbers. You will get back a letter telling you how many sheets will be required and how much they will cost (the charge per sheet is 20¢). You then order the listing sheets, enclosing a money order, payable to the Commissioner of Patents.

Next you will receive a number of sheets jampacked with patent numbers. That's all. Just the numbers. You can then order these patents by number. (As previously noted, the cost is 25¢ apiece for mechanical patents, 10¢ for design patents.)

There are two disadvantages to this method of searching. It will take a while, and it probably won't save you much money over a searcher's fee. In most cases you will end up buying a lot of patents useless to you. The average sub-classification contains 40 patents. At 25¢ apiece, that's $10. And since you usually have to study three or four sub-classifications, your cost is soon up to $30 or $40. Actually, you could have to look at a dozen sub-classifications, each of which might contain as many as 60 patents. One inventor in the field of industrial fasteners got a list of over 1000 possibly relevant patents.

At this stage of the game, if the list of patent numbers is long, you'd better back down and engage a searcher after all.

5

solving the model problem

The Patent Office does not require that you have a model (indeed, it won't even accept a model with your application), but it is a rare invention that can be "reduced to practice" without one. How else can you really know it works? It's an even rarer invention that can be *sold* without a model.

To these two basic needs for a model may be added a third: At some stage of Patent Office consideration of your application, the Patent Examiner may profess his skepticism of your invention's workability. He may then ask for proof, perhaps in the form of a look at the model, perhaps in the form of affidavits from credible witnesses who have seen—or, better yet, used— the invention.

This last was the way inventors George Schechter and Irwin Hirsch won their patent. They had invented a woman's shoe that uses no straps or ties to hold it onto the foot. Instead, a magnet embedded in the heel of the shoe clings to either a thin metal plate taped to the sole of the foot, or hosiery woven with metallic threads.

The patent Examiner expressed doubts that the shoes would really stay on, as the inventors claimed they would. Schechter and Hirsch were ready with convincing evidence. They had made up 20 pairs of the shoes and were able to get affidavits from the wearers. They got their patent.

• do manufacturers require models?

Do you need a model to demonstrate to manufacturers when you're trying to sell your invention? This is a question that often confronts the inventor.

A lot depends on the nature of your invention and just how interested the manufacturer may be in its basic principles. If your invention is simple, if its workability is apparent, then most manufacturers do not require a model. Of course, this assumes that the manufacturer can look at the drawings and be convinced your invention will work, just as you visualize it will.

Complicated machines are another matter. You can't be absolutely certain the machine will function just as you think it will. In a case we know, a man invented a wire-weaving machine. It had features of speed that interested several wire making manufacturers. From the inventor's blueprints it did appear the machine would work. But experienced engineers know too well they cannot depend on visualization or theory. To make a model of the machine would cost upwards of $25,-000, and even though the manufacturers felt the machine offered many advantages over anything on the market, they refused to advance the necessary money. The inventor couldn't afford it. So there was the end of another invention.

There's no one rule that can be laid down. If the invention is sufficiently interesting to the manufacturer, he may be willing to pay all the expenses of making a model. Sometimes a company will offer to build a model if the inventor will share the cost, perhaps paying it from his royalties. Each case is special. However, if your invention is highly complicated, you have to be able to prove that it will work and a model is the only sure way to do it.

● model making simplified

Many inventors are more troubled by the problem of making a model than they need be. There are many sources of assistance. One of the best ways to get help in making your model is to turn to the manufacturer of some component or material that will go into your invention.

We're surprised that so many inventors fail to utilize this readily available source of assistance. We've seen it make the vital difference in speeding an invention along the road to success. The company that developed the component which may find use in your invention has already gone through the arduous process of determining the limitations and capabilities of its product. In doing this it has amassed what can be a treasure trove of vital information for the inventor.

Look at the story of Harold Humes and his paper house. Humes, a writer with a technical turn of mind, didn't have all the knowledge he needed for building his new kind of dwelling. But a lot of his work had already been done for him. The chemists of the big concerns that produce treatments for making paper water-, fire-, vermin-, and just about anything-proof, did have it, and those companies had a definite stake in his success.

So when Humes got the idea that such paper would make a fine summer cottage, or low-cost home for underdeveloped areas, all he had to do was design corrugated, honeycombed panels and work out a method of fastening them together with metal straps.

The big chemical companies helped him with the rest. Humes estimates that he talked to a couple dozen "technical representatives" from the chemical and paper companies. They gave him valuable advice at every step of the way, telling him exactly what he could and couldn't do with paper.

Humes still put a lot of work into developing techniques for constructing paper pillars, floor, walls and roof, but the help given him made the day when he and his friends assembled the world's first paper house come a lot sooner and less expensively than if he'd carried it through on his own.

Finding just the right material or component can sometimes make your "reduction to practice" a snap. An illustration of this is the invention of Charles Powell. What he thought of was a piece of statuary which could be assembled by joining pre-molded components. The amateur, do-it-yourself "sculptor" would then cover this figure with a material which would hide the joints and give it a finished appearance. But what kind of material? Powell wanted to embed small particles of wood, metal, or stone in some kind of paint-like plastic, which would "set" after application.

At this point, Powell sought help from Bakelite Corporation. Yes, this chemical company had exactly the material he could use—a polymerized vinyl resin—and had embodied the pertinent information about it in the company's Technical Release No. 12.

Using this knowledge, which had cost the company much research effort, Powell was able to go ahead and in one stroke obtain both his working model and his invention. The part he needed help on had been "invented" for him. He had a completely dependable compound ready to market. In his patent application, Powell mentioned this resin by its trade name, taking care, of course, to state that similar compounds could be used.

If, like Powell, you have an invention (or even an idea) for which you think there may be an already developed component or material that may solve your model making problems, but don't know what that component is nor who might make it, turn to *Thomas' Register*, the inventor's friend. These huge volumes, with their 9,000-plus pages, can be consulted at almost any public library in the country. They list every manufacturing concern in the United States, cross-indexing them under the products they make. You look under the product heading that seems relevant to you and there you will find the names and addresses of all companies that might make what you're looking for.

In contacting any manufacturer for assistance, explain the general nature of your invention and detail the particular problem or problems on which you are having difficulty. You are likely to get a prompt and interested reply.

• having your model made for you

Maybe you lack the skill, the tools, or the know-how to make a model. Maybe you don't want to. Or maybe you want a more finished model than you could turn out yourself.

If you have the money to hire highly skilled labor to turn out a custom job, it is not hard to find someone to do it. In every good-sized city there are a number of shops that specialize in making models. You will find them listed under various classifications in the yellow pages of the telephone book. In Philadelphia, for instance, a recent edition lists 36 concerns under the heading "Model Makers—Invention and Scale." In New York City 64 firms are listed under "Model Makers—Industrial."

Many of these companies are makers of display models or other types of models that differ greatly from the models required by inventors. But advertisements on the same pages will generally indicate the ones that do work for inventors, and a telephone call will quickly tell you if any particular one can do the job you have in mind.

Another major classification in the yellow section is generally labeled "Machinists." In a large city there will be many listings here. Of course, only a few of them will be interested in handling the small non-production job of developing an invention. Again, advertisements will usually indicate those interested in this type of business.

Even in smaller communities, there is usually a machine shop which can take on a custom job. The local Chamber of Commerce may be able to offer suggestions if you cannot otherwise locate somebody to work for you.

Going outside your own community presents some difficulties, because you will have to expect to work closely with the mechanics or engineers of the firm you employ. If you do have to go to another city, try to find a firm which has done similar work in the past. They'll be able to work with less supervision from you.

You may be surprised at how much skilled assistance you can get, even in the smallest town. Machine shops in the community of Spring Lake, Michigan, built the model which enabled James Robbins to sell his coin-operated dry cleaning machine to a big firm.

This, incidentally, was a case in which near perfection in the model was necessary, so professionally machined parts were needed. The main value of Robbins' invention to Norge, the appliance maker which bought it, was that it was ready for the market, with very little further company research and development work called for. The company knew this would give it a big jump on the competition, inevitable now that Robbins had perfected his machine. The likelihood that another company could come up with one that didn't infringe his patent was great. Thus, with a perfected model, Robbins qualified for the sale that has brought him such big returns.

This may bring to your mind the question of the inventor's rights in something on which he has employed outside help. Fears that if you use such assistance you will not be the "true, sole, and only" inventor are groundless if you really do all the creative work.

Robbins performed all the inventive work on the dry cleaning machine (the machinists supplied only physical labor and mechanical skill), so he was the only inventor, and had to cut no one in on his patent rights.

If, however, one of the machinists had come up with novel ideas that were incorporated into the invention, Robbins would have been required to declare him a co-inventor in making his application for a patent.

● should you use your employer's facilities?

Puzzling to many employed inventors is the subject of using company facilities in "reducing to practice." If you are a technical employee, this is not likely to be a matter of question to you. You probably have a contract, a condition of employment, that calls for assigning your invention to the company. (See typical contract in the *Reference Guide.*) In that case, of course, you will avail yourself of all company facilities, since your employer has stated rights in your invention anyway.

However, if you are a non-technical employee, and have no such contract, you should be governed by the statement of Albert Woodruff Gray, a noted patent authority: "The general rule is that, in the absence of an express agreement by an employee to give an employer the benefit of an employee's genius, the employer has no interest in the patent issued to said employee, even though it can be said that his inventive power was stimulated by knowledge necessarily derived from his employment."

Suppose, however, you use actual company facilities, such as laboratory or shop equipment, in developing your invention and making a model? Let us say you are in the position in which an office executive in a midwestern plastic products company found himself. His invention was a sportsman's item unlike anything the company was engaged in making. Actually most of his work in developing his model was done in his own home workshop, but he did use company equipment in the shop on several occasions. He did so on his own time—during noon hours and holidays—and with the permission of a shop foreman.

Later, when he got a patent, the company asserted that, by virtue of his having used company equipment, it was entitled to "shop rights" and could make the invention if it wanted to. This particular matter was settled without reference to the courts, but it might well have ended up there if the company had not decided that it did not want to manufacture the invention after all.

Generally, if you use company facilities, your employer is entitled to these so-called "shop rights." This does not mean that the company owns the patent, nor that the inventor must assign it to the company, as he must do in cases where he has a contract to do so. It does mean that the employer has a non-exclusive license to use the invention in the course of his business, without payment of a royalty. The employer cannot license anyone else to use it, however. Only the inventor can do this, and he is free to do so, since the license to the employer is non-exclusive. However, in practice, he would be hampered in his sale to another company which might demand an exclusive license.

If you think it could be to your advantage to use your employer's facilities in the working up of your model, you would do well to talk to company officials about it. Indicate that you're working on an invention in such and such a field and would like to know what the company's attitude toward it might be. Would it demand shop rights if you availed yourself of any company facilities? Would the company be interested in considering purchase of such an invention if you should succeed in perfecting it? (Perhaps you'll thus painlessly find a possible buyer!)

Certainly you have nothing to lose by not getting things straight with your employer from the start. We've known of cases where the company has given an inventor much assistance, even though it had no legal stake in his invention.

The inventor of one of the century's most successful toys worked for a rubber company and actually developed his toy on company time, using company equipment. Since it was out of the concern's ordinary line of business, it cheerfully relinquished any claim to it and left him free to sell it to a toy maker. He collected over $300,000 in royalties.

is there a market
for your invention?

> "Many persons believe they can profit from their inventions merely by patenting them. This is a mistake. No one can profit from a patent unless it covers some feature which provides an improvement for which people are willing to pay."
>
> —*Patents and Inventions*
> U.S. Dept. of Commerce

You may as well face it. Less than half the inventions patented ever bring any financial return to their creators. Many of these should never have been patented. From the beginning they stood no chance in the marketplace.

It is essential to make a preliminary search to determine patentability; it is equally essential to make what we like to call a **marketability search.** Its purpose is to give you the answer to three vital questions that will determine whether you have an invention worth expenditure of the $300 or more it will cost you to get a patent. (See Chapter 7 for a discussion of such costs.)

These are the questions which must be answered:

- **Can it compete?**
- **Will they buy it?**
- **Can it be made at a price the buyers will pay?**

Yes, they sound obvious. Yet answering these three simple questions calls for doing something that all too few inventors do—getting outside yourself and looking at your invention as others will see it. Of course *you* are sold on it, but how does it look to the person who is going to use it, pay out money for it? How does it look to the clerk who may sell it? To the manufacturer you want to pay you a royalty for the right to make your invention?

Our experience tells us that there are three common mental obstacles that keep an inventor from making any kind of marketability search. They are:

• 1 • **The belief that it's not important.** The inventor is so convinced that his enthusiastic size-up of his invention is right that he doesn't feel it necessary to check up. However, almost all of the successful inventors we know have, in one way or another, market-checked their inventions. Many of them have found the market check enabled them to make changes in their inventions that improved both saleability and patentability.

• 2 • **The fear that somebody will steal his invention.** This is the nightmare that haunts inventors all along the line. Patent Office officials, patent attorneys, and invention brokers all observe it, and all agree that it is unreasonable. Many an inventor who knows he should get market information about his invention, fears to do it because he's afraid that if he talks about it, or shows it to anybody, someone will copy it and rush off to the Patent Office. *If* you followed the precautions we outline in Chapter 2 *you have nothing whatsoever to fear in making a marketability check.*

• 3 • **He doesn't know how to go about it.** That's an understandable situation. If you are a doctor, lawyer, teacher, housewife, executive, or in any of the innumerable walks of life from which today's independent inventors are drawn, you can hardly be expected to know how to survey the market possibilities of your invention. And you are hardly in a position to do what big companies do when they think about putting a new product on the market—hire a marketing concern to check for you. Fortunately, it is possible for you to conduct a do-it-yourself market search successfully, at little or no cost, right in your own community. We can't spell out all the details of checking your particular invention, but the suggestions that follow should help.

● can it compete?

You must find out whether your invention is good enough to compete successfully with any and all other products that perform the same function it does.

It may be possible that there is no competition. You are fortunate if your invention is unique and does something no other product can do. Dr. Horton's *Slumbertone* was an invention possessing this enviable attribute. There were no other devices for soothing small babies. Al Creighton, the Boston economist who invented *Plastic Steel,* had another such unique invention. When it came on the market there were no other putty-like metal compounds that hardened on contact with air.

If you are lucky enough to have an invention with no competition, the question "Can it compete?" obviously has no importance to your analysis of its marketability. You can proceed with getting the answers to the two other basic questions of marketability. But the odds are high against your having such an invention. More likely your brainchild will be vying with anything from one to scores of products for sales and profits, when and if it is put on the market.

First you have to find out what the competitive products are and how well your invention compares with them. As the result of your preliminary search you already have some facts about your competition. You may have learned of several inventions (whether they were ever marketed or not) that do what your invention does. You've got a start on your investigation.

But it's just a start. You probably don't have all the patents on devices that perform the same function as your invention. (Remember, the searcher was checking to see whether the structure of your invention was new. But there may be inventions which are still *commercially* competitive.) And there may also be unpatented products that will compete with your invention. These obviously would not be turned up in a patent search.

So do what far too few inventors do—systematically seek out your competition. You should want to know about every single product your invention will have to compete with.

The most logical place to begin looking for this competition is in stores that carry merchandise that does what your invention does. These will be the same stores that will sell your invention if you do go ahead and put it on the market.

Don't just look on the shelves. Ask the clerks, or better yet, the person who does the store's buying, about products in the line of your invention. Pump these people for every bit of information you can get. What are these products like? How much do they cost? What advantages or disadvantages do they possess? How do they sell?

While you are at these same stores, you can probably make use of another competition-discovering technique. Ask if you may look at the store's wholesale or distributors' catalogs. These contain lists and specifications of a large variety of products in a given field.

Trade journals such as *Hardware Age, Toy and Hobby World, The Sporting Goods Dealer,* and *The Housewares Buyer,* give you, in their advertisements and new products columns, a wealth of information about the latest in potential competition.

There may be other magazines that can give you a picture of the competition. If your invention will be used primarily by hunters, a survey of the products advertised in *Sports Afield,* *Field and Stream,* and *Outdoor Life* is obviously in order. If it's an invention that will be used by do-it-yourselfers, *Popular Science, Popular Mechanics, Science and Mechanics* and *Mechanix Illustrated* are logical publications to consult.

When you are sure that you know what the competition is, it is time to proceed with the analysis of the relative worth of your invention.

The most important question to answer here is: **How well does your invention do its job as compared to its competitors?** The best way of answering this question is to get hold of the other products and test them against your invention.

Beulah Henry, the United States' most prolific woman inventor (she has more than 40 patents to her credit) did just this when she came up with a new kind of mailing and return envelope, which she figured would save a lot of money for bulk mailers such as utility companies and stores that bill thousands of customers. She knew that there was one basic criterion of workability—speed. Would her envelope really speed up mailing and therefore cut costs?

She found her envelope could be folded, filled, and addressed twice as fast as any competitive envelope. With the additional knowledge that her envelope would save on paper costs—since it, unlike any other envelope, used only one piece of paper for the mailing envelope, the statement, and the return mailer— she proceeded with patenting. The answer to the question of whether her envelope was better than its competition was an obvious yes.

But of course not all inventions subjected to workability comparison prove to be superior. We've seen many situations where even a casual check was enough to make an inventor realize that, though his invention might be patentable, it definitely flunked the superior workability test. (There's nothing in patent law, incidentally, that says an invention has to be *better* than an existent one to be patented. But there is an unwritten law of marketability which says it has to be better in some respect if it's to stand a chance of commercial success.)

Take the case of the inventor who came up with what he felt was a superior window-washing device, on the order of a squeegee. He did what few inventors do—went around to hardware stores and bought several different types of similar devices. To his dismay, he found that some washed windows both better and faster than his own device. End of invention. He was dejected, but not nearly so much as he'd have been if he'd gone on, patented his window cleaner (which he probably could have done, it being quite an original structural approach), and then spent time and money trying to market a device that would have to compete with superior products already on the market.

Workability, of course, is not the only consideration which determines the relative value of your invention. Other assets can be just as important as how well your invention works— and can make a "no better" invention, as far as function goes, a "better" invention when it comes to sales.

Ease of use is one valuable marketing quality that your invention can possess. The housewife who invented *Jonny-Mop* didn't have an invention that got toilet bowls cleaner than other methods. But she did have an invention that made the washing easier, and that was enough to make her invention a resounding commercial success.

Compactness can give your invention a decisive advantage. The man who invented a small battery charger which could be permanently installed under the hood of a car didn't improve the quality of battery-charging, but the small size of his device gave it saleability.

Low price is an obvious asset. One of the biggest invention success stories of the 20th Century is *Toni* home permanent. *Toni* didn't give women a better permanent than the beauty parlor did, but it certainly made a permanent a lot less expensive. And, of course, all do-it-yourself inventions are given market appeal by the financial savings they promise buyers.

There are other points of superiority that can give your invention an edge over the competition—aesthetic appearance, durability, disposability, or, in some cases, sheer novelty.

● will they buy it?

So you've satisfied yourself that you have an invention that will make a good, competitive product. You still don't have an answer to the question of whether the potential user will find it really worthwhile. Will he want it enough to buy it?

To find out, go to the consumer himself and get at least a sampling of reactions, either favoring or disfavoring your invention. This may well involve making or having made a model or several samples. This is an investment in time and money which we consider to be about the wisest an inventor can make in the case of most consumer-type inventions. (We discussed model and sample making in Chapter 5.)

Such a consumer test was employed by George Schechter and Irwin Hirsch, who developed the magnetic shoe described in the previous chapter. The inventors made up 20 pairs, which they gave to as many women, who agreed to wear them off and on over a period of one year. This tested them under all conditions and produced reports of consumer acceptance convincing to manufacturers to whom the shoe was later licensed.

Ross Williams, who invented *Wash 'n Dri*, the lotion impregnated towel which permits travelers to wash without water, also used this method of market analysis. Williams made up 250 samples by hand and bought a ticket to Bermuda on Pan American, arranging to pass out samples to his fellow passengers, along with a "rating card."

The travelers all liked his invention and Williams knew he had a potential moneymaker. In this case not only did Williams find that he had a good invention—he also made a sale. The airline immediately order 400,000 packets of *Wash 'n Dri* towels for distribution to its passengers.

Even big companies, which are better able to afford losses than is the independent inventor, customarily go one step further in testing new consumer products. It's not enough to know that people *like* something; you've got to find out if they'll *buy* it. This is how one inventor did it:

John Leutzinger of Seattle, had a small, profitable business selling pre-finished plywood panels to do-it-yourselfers. He was often asked the same question. What, his customers wanted to know, did you do with the nail holes after you put the panels in place? Filling compounds on the market never seemed to match the finish of the panels.

Leutzinger went to work and finally came up with a compound that could be produced in stick form and colored to match almost any shade of wood finish. You could rub it over nail holes and they disappeared.

Leutzinger knew that his invention possessed a characteristic no other product had, and he knew it worked because he had tried it himself. But how would it sell?

This inventor was fortunate in having his own store for test-selling his invention. Soon people who had bought one *Putty-Stik* came running back to buy more. This was consumer acceptance on a hard cash level.

Reassured by his trial run, Leutzinger rounded up capital and proceeded to go into the business of manufacturing *Putty-Stik* in quantities suitable for nationwide selling.

Henry Ruzza, a civil engineer of Eau Claire, Wisconsin, didn't have a store when he used the test sale in the market evaluation of his invention—a bricklaying tool he christened

Automason. He had to work for his customers, and the way he did it makes a good example of how you can utilize the test sale even if you don't have commercial facilities at hand.

Ruzza knew that his tool solved a number of problems and had a number of advantages. It would enable an amateur bricklayer to lay bricks faster, with absolute evenness, without wasting mortar, and without scraping his hands.

But would its potential users actually buy it? Ruzza had a few *Automasons* made by a local machine shop, then ran low-cost ads in small-circulation magazines. He received orders for 20. He sold more when he got a write-up in an engineering magazine's new product section.

Though *Automason* was offered with an unconditional money-back guarantee, not one of the tools was returned to Ruzza. And they sold readily at a price many times the cost of quantity manufacture. He knew he had a saleable invention, one that met every commercial requirement. He knew because he had given it the real payoff test; he had actually sold it.

The use of a test sale could have saved one inventor we know at least $15,000 and a lot of grief.

He had a novelty device, and he was so convinced of its appeal that he commissioned a machine shop to make them for him in mass lots, making no market check whatsoever.

He then put his device in department stores on a consignment basis. The gadget fell flat. He sold something like 200 of them. The last we knew, his garage, his workshop and his attic were still stacked with boxes of unsold units.

● can it be made at a price they'll pay?

How deeply should an inventor go into the question of production costs? If you're thinking at all of setting up your own business to make and sell your invention, very deeply indeed. Then you'll want to take the steps we outline in Chapter 14.

However, if you have no intention of starting your own concern, your check-up will be much more casual and there's no reason why you should put great effort into checking the fine points of production. All you really want is an estimate—and it can be a very rough one—of what it's going to cost to produce your invention.

If you've had your model made up by a machine shop, or have had a machine shop run off some samples, you'll already have a good start toward learning production costs. Check with the same concern to see what it would charge for runs of various quantities.

How close do they come to the formula which says that manufacturing costs must come out somewhere between ⅕th and ¼th of the selling price? If you have an item which must sell for around $5 (your competition and consumer check should tell you about the price range) and the estimate comes out $2, you know that's too high. You'll have to check some more.

Is this high estimate made by a plant that doesn't really have the equipment? Is it on runs much smaller than those which would be used if the product was in actual production? Is the model on which the firm is basing the estimate ill-designed for production? Could it use ready-made component parts which would be cheaper? Could it be changed so it would require less expensive dies? Could less expensive materials be used in it?

If it turns out that the estimate falls roughly within such a formula, you need hardly do any further checking. You've got enough information to incorporate in your discussions with any prospects for your invention.

your patent attorney

An inventor makes no more important decision than his choice of a patent attorney, or agent, to aid him in getting a patent.

If you've already engaged an attorney to make your search, and if you are satisfied with the way he has handled it, you will be well advised to keep him and go forward into the next steps in getting your patent. However, if you have any reservations, you are under no obligation to retain this particular attorney.

A basic question confronting you is the one of whether your patent attorney or agent should be in Washington, or in or near your home community. If you're like most inventors you will probably find that things will work out better if you choose the latter. A certain amount of personal consultation with your attorney may be helpful, or downright necessary. It's more important that the attorney be close to you than that he be close to the Patent Office, since getting a patent is not something done by personal appearance, as in a court.

Of course, in interferences or infringement cases, personal appearances are called for, and sometimes having a Washington attorney might be an advantage. However, these are unlikely developments, and are matters in which you might well engage different, or additional, attorneys.

Another basic question is: **Should you choose an attorney or**

an agent? To be registered, an agent must meet the same requirements demanded of attorneys, that is, he "shall establish
to the satisfaction of the Commissioner that he is of good moral
character and high repute and possessed of the legal, scientific
and technical qualifications necessary to enable him to render
valuable service, and is otherwise competent to advise and
assist" the inventor. However, the agent is not an attorney, and
therefore cannot prepare any legal instruments such as assignments, licensing agreements, etc. Nor can he carry out patent
litigation in the courts. However, these services are not part
of prosecuting the patent application and an agent—generally
an engineer—will usually be as satisfactory as an attorney. A
registered agent, that is.

We cannot emphasize that word "registered" too strongly.
For if you fall into the hands of an un-registered agent, you can
be in for trouble.

● beware of "gyp" agents

If you see an advertisement by anyone offering to make a
patent search or to assist you in getting a patent, you know at
once that this person or firm is NOT registered by the Patent
Office. **No one registered to represent an applicant on official
business at the Patent Office is allowed to advertise.** Therefore,
anyone who does advertise his services *is not registered.* It's
as simple as that, and we've repeated it because not knowing
this fact has cost many inventors much money and heartache.

Now it is true that an unregistered person can make a search
for you, because anyone who wishes to do so is entitled to
use the services of the Search Room, as we pointed out in
Chapter 4. This person can also, it is true, "prepare" your
application for you. We put the words "prepare" in quotes
because it's anybody's guess whether your application is properly made out and your claims effectively drawn. With such

an unregistered person you have no recourse whatsoever, because he is in no way subject to the rules of ethics and standards of technical competence set up by the Patent Office—the rules and standards that do apply to registered practitioners.

After such a person has produced a patent application for you, he cannot go any further. He dumps the whole matter into your lap, sending the application to you to sign and mail in to the Patent Office. A registered attorney or agent does, of course, handle all the aspects of getting the application to the Patent Office.

But this is minor compared with what happens afterwards, a dismaying experience that has befallen a good many inventors who have been taken in by the blandishments of "we'll get your patent for you" racketeers. You've paid your money, as much or even more than you'd have paid a legitimate, registered practitioner. Yet here you are, with no representative to carry on your case for you. When the Patent Office notifies you of the first official action (see Chapter 9) you're on the spot. You have to reply, perhaps re-writing all your claims, and you have no one to speak for you.

If you write to the unregistered operator who prepared your application, he may not answer your letter at all. Or, if he does, he will tell you there's nothing he can do for you. At this late date you'll have to go out and hire a registered practitioner, who will come into the case wholly unfamiliar with your invention; or you'll have to present your own case before the Patent Office—a nearly impossible task for the layman. If an offer is made to "help" you with the amendments now necessary, the same cumbersome process must be followed. The unregistered operator cannot deal with the Patent Office directly at this point any more than he could have earlier. Therefore he must do his work—competent or incompetent—in amending your patent, and then send it back for you to submit to the Patent Office.

For all this he has an explanation that convinces many inventors—"*You* deal directly with the Patent Office," he says. "No go-betweens." As if that is an advantage!

Mind you, these unregistered operators who leave you in the lurch stay well within the law. They do what they say they will. They do not state that they will prepare your application for you; only that they will "have" it prepared. Similar weasel wording protects them—but not *you*. The Patent Office itself has no authority over them, since, in its eyes, they do not exist; they are subject to no discipline by the American Patent Law Association which governs the ethical conduct of its members.

While some practitioners who advertise (and who, therefore, are unregistered) may have some technical qualifications, such as engineering degrees, or even backgrounds as patent examiners, their inability to deal directly with the Patent Office makes their services a poor investment for any inventor.

There is another grave danger in dealing with the unregistered practitioner, even for a patent search, and that is the possibility that he'll lure you into seeking a patent you shouldn't be trying to get at all. As noted in Chapter 4, after a hasty search (advertised at low rates), he'll blithely inform you that he has found nothing to conflict with your invention. He'll urge you to go full speed ahead with the patent application—which he will make up for you, of course. Just send him your $250, or $350, or whatever figure he thinks he stands a chance of extracting from you.

To see how it works out, witness a recent independent investigation. To four gyp operators the investigator sent a description of an invention, accompanied by crude drawings. Actually, description and drawings were based on an existent patent which had been issued years earlier. (The owner of the patent was cooperating in the test.) All four of the recipients cashed the check sent them for the low priced search. And all four reported that they had made a search and found no patent covering such an invention. All indicated that, in view of this "fact," the inventor should proceed at once to apply for a patent.

When the same description and drawings were submitted to a legitimate patent attorney, who was asked to make a search at a regular fee, he found the patent on which they were based, reported that it was almost identical, and indicated flatly that there would be no use in seeking a patent on the device.

There could hardly be a more dramatic demonstration of the wisdom and importance of dealing with a registered attorney or agent. The searches made by the con men of the patent world were obviously either fraudulent or so faulty that they could not have been made by competent people. Yet these very persons were requesting inventors to hand over hundreds of dollars for processing their patent applications!

● what will your attorney charge?

Legal fees loom large in the minds of inventors. Perhaps you've heard tales of how high they are and have been scared off by these reports. Actually, the charges made by most patent attorneys are rather modest compared to other costs nowadays.

If you've already paid your attorney for your preliminary search, that will be taken into consideration when he sets his fee for seeking a patent on your invention. Fees vary somewhat from attorney to attorney, but a fairly typical fee for a simple device—say a household item—would be around $350. This will cover drawing up your application, supervising the drawings, and filing. (You actually pay for drawings and the filing fee separately, as per an itemized bill you receive from your attorney.) The cost for this basic service may run much higher if your invention is more complex, if the application is necessarily long, or the claims difficult to draw up. However, no reputable attorney will object to giving you an exact estimate of cost for these services in advance. As soon as he has studied the original description of your invention, and pondered the results of the preliminary search, he will know pretty closely just how long it's going to take him to draw up the application.

That may vary greatly from patent to patent in the same field. We know of one case where two very similar devices presented entirely different problems. One required a five-page application, with seven claims, and references to five other patents. The other was simply done in a page and a half and involved only three claims. The longer one, quite rightly, cost $500; the shorter one $350. Big industrial firms with highly complex patents have legal fees running into many thousands of dollars. Indeed, the independent inventor with the really big invention may find himself having to pay out the same kind of money.

Beyond these predictable costs, there is an X factor in what your total attorney's fees will be before you actually get your patent. Neither your attorney nor anyone else can foresee what's going to happen to your application once it's in the Patent Office. As explained in Chapter 9, your patent will probably require one or more amendments. Your attorney's charges for these are not part of the original agreed upon fee mentioned above; he will have to charge you for them.

If the amendments are simple, the additional fee for each one may run as little as $100. You shouldn't take the view that these amendments are a result of something your lawyer did wrong in the first place. It's part of the normal, orderly process by which patents are obtained. You should expect to have this additional expense and bear with the fact that it isn't 100% ascertainable in advance.

However, your attorney will be glad to talk about it. If he doesn't bring the subject up, you should. It's well to have some definite understanding that his charge will run within certain limitations for his work on the amendments. A common basis is

$100 a day for his services, although some attorneys may customarily charge more.

Since several amendments are possible, just how much your attorney may have to charge before you finally get your patent can only be estimated. Beyond that is the possibility of an interference case, in which it is necessary for you to fight a rival inventor whose application conflicts with yours. This will call for a personal appearance by the attorney, and is also quite unpredictable as to duration or amount of work involved in developing your case. A fee of $100 to $150 a day is a fairly common charge, and only in the case of an extremely complicated and valuable invention would more than a day or two be involved.

Here is a tabulation of the legal expenses involved in obtaining a typical patent for a small sporting goods device:

Search	$ 50.
Drawings	60.
Attorney's fee for application	350.
First amendment	100.
Second amendment	150.
	$710.

● trust your attorney

Once you've chosen an attorney, you must be prepared to place complete confidence in him.

He has to know all about your invention, and understand it thoroughly. He is going to perform a task that can make or break your invention. If you give him the help he needs from you, he'll be able to do his job better. If you fail to trust him and give him what he needs, it can make the road to getting a patent a lot more rocky than it has to be.

An unreasonable fear nags at many inventors. "How do I know my attorney won't steal my invention?" they ask. The truth is that there is absolutely no case on record in which an attorney did "steal" an invention. And you can be very sure that if one ever had, it *would* be on record. The Commissioner of Patents maintains a grievance committee to which are referred any complaints made by inventors or other interested parties. This committee can recommend suspension of an attorney or agent and hand over to law enforcement authorities any information that might lead to an indictment.

(Here again there comes up the question of the extreme importance of dealing with a *registered* attorney or agent. If he is not registered, the Commissioner of Patents has no control over his conduct. Of course, even an unregistered person is subject to the laws of the land; you could bring suit against him, but the burden would be entirely on you.)

You must realize that any registered attorney has his entire career at stake. He has had to meet stringent requirements to prove himself competent to practice in the first place. He certainly is not going to risk ruining his professional life by attempting something that he, of all people, knows best cannot be done.

Is it possible that an attorney might try to "steal" *part* of your invention, by claiming that he had made contributions to it, and was therefore entitled to be a co-inventor and share in the proceeds? No, this cannot occur because the law provides that any assistance given you by a registered attorney or agent is solely your property. In practice, many attorneys do make major contributions to inventors, suggesting modifications which could lead to a stronger set of claims.

8

applying for your patent

When you have your first meeting with your attorney to talk about your patent application, you should be able to give him a clear, complete description of your invention. Not just a verbal one, but a written one, as concise and accurate as you can make it, complete with drawings.

Any detail of your invention that isn't disclosed to your attorney will not be embodied in any eventual patent claims. And, of course, if it is not in the claims it will not be protected by your patent.

The disastrous results that can ensue from concealing some feature of your invention from your attorney (and therefore from the Patent Office) can be no more dramatically illustrated than by the case of one inventor of an industrial drilling machine, the most important feature of which was the contour of the drill's cutting edge.

This inventor patented his machine (which had other patentable features) without mentioning the cutting edge. For a while he enjoyed considerable success with his machine, since the cutting edge accomplished a long-sought-for result.

Then someone else started making drills with that cutting edge. The inventor hastened to his patent attorney, demanding that an infringement suit be brought against the competitor, who was taking a large share of his market.

The attorney, as he had a perfect right to do, blew up. Why, he asked, hadn't the inventor told him about the cutting edge in the first place, if that was the valuable feature of the invention?

Because, the inventor replied, he hadn't known that this particular aspect of his drill could be patented and therefore hadn't wanted to disclose it for fear someone would steal it. But it was still his invention, wasn't it? He could keep others from making it, couldn't he?

It wasn't his property any more. He had been selling his drill for more than a year, and it had therefore passed into the public domain. Since the cutting edge was not claimed in the patent, he had no protection whatsoever, other than the uncomforting knowledge that no one else could get a patent on it.

● parts of a patent application

To be accepted by the Patent Office and placed on file, a patent application must include:

—a written document containing a petition for patent, an "oath" which states that you are the true inventor of what you describe in your application, a "specification" which gives a full description of your invention, and your "claims," which state exactly, no more, no less, what particular features you seek patent protection for.

—a drawing or drawings that depict the structure of your invention, wherever a drawing is possible. A drawing is required on any mechanical, design, or plant patent, for example, but not on applications for chemical processes.

—a $30 filing fee, payable to the Commissioner of Patents, plus $1 for each "claim" exceeding 20. This fee is paid by you over and above your attorney's fees.

● petition and oath

The petition is merely a formality, but it is required by law. It usually comes at the beginning of your patent application and requests that the U.S. Government grant you "letters patent" on your invention.

The oath, as we said above, states that you believe yourself to be the first, true, and only inventor of what is described in your application.

When more than one person has contributed to an invention (other than your patent attorney), a joint petition and oath must be filed.

No one who did not assist in the inventive process can be claimed as a co-inventor. Thus, your financial backers, if you have any, are not co-inventors, if all they supplied was money. Nor are any workmen you employed to build your invention, if all they gave to it was labor and mechanical skill. Invention is defined by law as a *mental*, not a *mechanical*, process.

If you are not sure whether assistance you got from anyone qualifies as co-invention, be sure you discuss this point with your attorney, telling him exactly what the other person or persons did contribute. He will be able to tell you where you stand.

The penalty for claiming someone as a co-inventor who isn't, or for not listing someone who is, can be severe—invalidation of any patent or patents obtained. So be careful on this point.

● the specification

The specification proper is a full verbal description of your invention. It is usually divided into five parts, which are arranged in the following order:

—the title of invention. This is a brief "name-tag" that is descriptive of your invention. For an idea of what these name-tags are usually like, look at some patents. "A New and Improved Method of . . . ," "A Process for . . . ," and "A Portable Handtool for . . ." are examples of common phraseologies.

—a brief, general description of invention. This states its broad nature and its uses, or, as they are called in patent jargon, its "objects." When stating the objects of your invention, your attorney is partly concerned with getting across its point of superiority over the "prior art."

—a brief description of the views in drawing, telling, let's say, that Fig. 1 is a plain top view, Fig. 2 an exploded side view, etc.

—a detailed description of invention. This is a full, precise explanation of each part of your invention and of the interactions of the parts. In other words, it details how your invention is constructed. It is meant to be read in connection with the drawings, so that the drawings and the verbal description are mutually explanatory. Both new and old elements of your invention are included in this description—that is, both elements you have invented and ones you have not.

—the claim or claims. These are exact statements of the mechanical structures, chemical processes or whatever it is that you claim as your invention.

● preparing the patent drawings

Patent drawings are a very special form of mechanical illustration. The rules governing the ways in which they must be drawn are complex and many. You will find "Patent Office Requirements for Drawings" in the *Reference Guide*. A glance at these specifications will show you that patent drawing requires considerable knowledge and skill. If you are a really good draftsman, you might be justified in making your own, but chances are you'd be better off to have a professional make them for you.

You can hire a freelance patent draftsman, who will charge from $50 to $75 a sheet, a modest price considering the exacting demands. Or you may use the services of a Patent Office draftsman. This will cost less ($25 a sheet), but it may take many months for you to get your drawings.

It's not often that we would recommend either of these two courses. The third and best way of getting your patent drawings is to let your attorney choose the draftsman, one to whom he can stress the novelty of your invention and with whom he can work closely to make sure that the specification and the drawings bear each other out. (Some attorneys make drawings for their clients themselves.) If there are any changes or corrections to be made, your attorney will detail them to the draftsman.

When your attorney receives the drawings from the draftsman (at this stage they will be in pencil, to be inked in later), he will painstakingly number every part of your invention as shown in the drawings. If a certain part appears in more than one drawing it still has only one number, as required by Patent Office regulation.

Then he writes the detailed description of your invention, referring to every part by the number it has been given on the drawings. Each part which appears in the drawings must be mentioned in the specification; conversely, each part mentioned in the specification must appear in the drawings when the application is submitted.

In writing the detailed description, your attorney makes sure that the structure of your invention is fully explained in a logical manner that will make the Patent Office examiner who reads your application able to understand it as completely and quickly as possible.

When the first draft of the detailed description is completed, the attorney will send a copy of the drawings and the description to you. You should check them carefully, first to see whether each part of your invention is numbered on the drawings and mentioned in the description and to make sure that the description and drawings accurately represent what you have invented.

If you have ideas as to changes you would like made in the drawings, you should draw the suggested corrections to the best of your ability on a tissue overlay. Make no changes in the drawings themselves. Enclose your reasons for wishing the changes when you give the drawings back to your attorney.

If you have suggestions as to changes that should be made in the specification, type them out on a separate sheet of paper and give your reasons. If there are disagreements between you and your attorney at this point, further consultation may be in order.

● the claims

The claims of a patent define what your patent gives you the right to "exclude others from making, selling or using" in this country. They are precise statements of what you have invented.

Your attorney tries to get the Patent Office to "allow" (that is, to grant you) the broadest possible claims on your invention. The broader the claims, the more valuable is your patent.

It is in the writing of the claims that a patent attorney really puts all of his legal acumen to work. In addition to making them as broad as possible, he has to make sure they are airtight.

It is possible by the use of one wrong word to make a patent worthless.

To make your claims broad, your attorney tries to avoid the use of "restrictive language." To see what this means, let us suppose you have an invention that utilizes a sheet of rubber under tension. Your attorney would try to get the Patent Office to allow some such phrase as "means for providing resiliency." Thus the claim would "dominate" any apparatus which used, say, nylon for the same purpose as your rubber sheet.

He will avoid the naming of raw materials. If he must name a material to make a patent clear, he will use a phrase such as "preferably of aluminum" instead of just plain "aluminum," thereby making sure that your claim dominates the use of any other material for the same purpose.

It is not always possible for an attorney to get you broad claims, especially if there are numerous patents in "the prior art." Remember that you can claim nothing which has been previously claimed, by you or by any other inventor. However, your attorney is likely to submit a first claim in your application of an extremely broad nature—a claim which he knows will not be allowed.

In fact, for reasons which we will explain in the next chapter, all of the claims that he makes are tentative and may well be disallowed on their first encounter with the patent examiner.

There is one kind of claim the Patent Office definitely will not allow. This is the so-called "functional claim." You cannot make any claim which does not detail a structure, but which merely states a purpose. In other words, if you have invented a new potato peeler, you cannot make any claim such as "means for peeling potatoes." This states your invention's function, or purpose.

The claims are the area in which the do-it-yourself inventor who elects to be his own attorney is likely to run into the most trouble. No less august a body than the U.S. Supreme Court has pointed out two disastrous mistakes that amateurs often make: **They claim too much, or, what is far worse, fail to claim what they have actually invented.** In other words, inventors often fail to obtain patents on patentable inventions or they obtain patents that give them no protection whatsoever.

In one case an inventor obtained a patent on a bandsaw and neglected to claim his clutch mechanism, which was the most valuable feature of his invention.

To add insult to injury he was unable to go back and re-apply for a patent on this feature. Since the clutch was described in his patent, even though not claimed, he could not get a patent. He had, weird as it may sound, "anticipated" himself.

● application for a design patent

An application for a design patent consists primarily of the drawings, showing the design. The drawings must be of extremely high caliber and must be a literal representation of the design as it will appear on the item of manufacture as displayed for sale.

Only one design may be included in a single application.

There is only one claim, and it states that you claim "the ornamental design for a _____, as shown," or that you claim this design "substantially as shown."

The fee for a design patent application depends on the length of time you wish your patent to run. A 3½-year application costs $10; a 7-year one, $15; and one for 14 years, $30.

● application for a plant patent

An application for a plant patent follows the same general outline as that for a mechanical patent. The specification of such an application should contain a full description of the plant for which the patent is sought.

Drawings, paintings, or photographs of the plant must be included in the application. If color is one of the distinguishing characteristics of your plant, the drawings or photographs must be in color. Current estimates for the kind of drawings required run from $75 to $150.

There is only one claim in a plant patent. You claim simply the plant, as you have described it.

The filing fee is the same as for a mechanical patent—$30.

● applying for a foreign patent

There is no such thing as an "international patent." A United States patent grants rights which extend in its territory alone. (No foreign patent is effective in this country either.) If you wish to obtain patent protection in one or more foreign countries, you must file separately in each of them, in accordance with the requirements set up by their governments.

Patent law, and the rights a patent afford, vary widely around the world. In most foreign countries, a series of fees must be paid after issuance of the patent, in increasing annual payments. Also, most foreign countries require that a patented invention must be manufactured (not just sold) in that country within three years after patent issuance, or the patent becomes void or subject to compulsory licensing.

There is an international treaty relating to patents. Forty countries, including the U.S., are parties to it. The treaty provides that the countries will provide the same patent rights to foreign citizens as to their own citizens. Further, it provides that if an application for patent is made in any signatory country, and an application is made in a second country within one year of the first, the date of the first application shall be the effective filing date in the second country.

The Patent Office cannot help you get a foreign patent, nor can a U.S. lawyer. You must hire an attorney in the country in which you wish to get a patent. This, however, can be done through any one of a number of U.S. firms which maintain relations with lawyers in other countries.

If you wish to apply for a patent in a foreign country within six months after filing your U.S. application, you must have a license from the Commissioner of Patents. This license may be given in response to a letter you write to the Commissioner. After six months have elapsed, no such license is required, unless the Patent Office has ordered you to keep your invention secret for reasons of national security.

getting your patent

Many inventors look upon the Patent Office as an enemy, a hostile bureaucracy which delights in placing obstacles in their way.

The two most bitter complaints are that it takes too long (average: three years) to process an application through to a patent, and that there is too much red tape.

The first of these is a legitimate complaint. It does take too long to get a patent. The Patent Office is woefully overloaded with work and woefully understaffed. There are something like a quarter of a million applications in the works at any given moment, and only around 1000 examiners to handle them. That makes an average of 250 applications on each examiner's desk.

However, at the time of the writing of this book, plans are under way to automate some phases of the patent process by feeding all patents into the memory banks of computers. When this computerized system goes into operation, the novelty of a new invention can be decided upon by the computers and the business of the Patent Office will be speeded up considerably.

As for the red tape, unfortunately a lot of it is unavoidable. The Patent Office is a governmental body, and it must proceed by rule and regulation to insure an orderly legal process. The regulations were set up to protect, not hinder, you. We can imagine the loud screams that would go up from any inventor who was denied a patent because the Patent Office had not abided by the minutest detail of the established procedure.

It is our hope that this chapter, in which we will tell you what happens after your application is accepted and placed on file to wait its turn for processing, will give you a sympathetic understanding of the Patent Office and its method of operation.

● the examiner's search

It takes, on the average, six months for you to hear anything from the Patent Office, other than to get an acknowledgement that your application has been received. It takes this long for your application to come to the top of the pile.

What you receive then is called the "first official action." This is the examiner's statement as to whether he considers any of your claims allowable.

The examiner is a Patent Office employee. He is an intelligent, well-trained man, who has no personal stake in either granting or not granting you a patent. You will probably never know his name and it is almost certain that you will never see him.

The first thing the examiner does when he takes up consideration of your application is to make a search. He takes your application and, in effect, compares it, claim by claim, with all U.S. patents previously issued, all foreign patents, and all applications for patents presently pending, to see whether what you have invented is really new.

This search, as you can see, is similar in form to the preliminary search we talked about in Chapter 4. But it is much more extensive and detailed. Not only does the examiner investigate more material than the preliminary searcher, he also probes more deeply into it.

The examiner is certain to come up with patents, relating to the novelty of your invention, which the preliminary searcher never even looked at. This is not grounds for you to complain that your searcher did a careless job. You didn't pay him to make this kind of search. Neither is it grounds for you to protest that the Patent Office is going too far afield to discover inventions that supposedly anticipate your own. If there are any that do, you certainly want to know about them. You'd be pretty disgruntled if you were issued a patent which later turned out to be invalid.

● the first official action

When the examiner has finished his search he writes a letter to your attorney. Copies of this "first official action" are kept by the Patent Office, and are included in the case history of your application, as are all other exchanges between your attorney and the Patent Office. These become a matter of public record, and after a patent is granted may be viewed by other inventors and attorneys, along with your original application.

In his letter, the examiner gives his decision as to the allowability of each claim in turn. In many cases he does something quite startling and unnerving to an inventor unacquainted with Patent Office procedures. **He simply rejects every claim!** This dismaying action, however, is just part of the give-and-take process that is aimed at giving you a really solid patent, and is not as bad as it seems.

Here's why: When he drew your claims to begin with, your lawyer knew that he was making them on the basis of limited knowledge—that of the preliminary search paid for by the inventor. This search, as we've said, could not have the thoroughness of the examiner's search.

At this point, however, your attorney has the benefit of this thorough search. He has known all along that the wealth of prior art, and the many foreign patents turned up by the examiner, will make it necessary to modify the claims for your invention.

In his claim-by-claim rejection, the examiner cites his exact reasons. He'll designate the particular patents that he believes conflict, and just what in them conflicts. He may also allege that your invention "lacks novelty," and cite, as the reason for this conclusion, a kind of reference that is the peculiar creation of the patent examiner.

This is the so-called hypothetical reference, which an examiner "makes up" out of a number of actual references.

Suppose you have entered a claim that covers parts A, B, C, and D working together. An examiner might find part A mentioned in a French patent, part B in a pending application, part C in an out-of-print mechanics textbook, and part D in last month's issue of some technical journal. The structures in which these parts are elsewhere embodied need not be in any way like your invention for the examiner to construct a hypothetical reference which says that your claim is invalid because your combination of parts (none of which is new) is "obvious." (Remember that patents are not granted on anything "obvious to people in the art." See Chapter 3.)

The lengths to which the principle of hypothetical reference could be carried may seem quite frightening. Most, if not all, mechanical inventions utilize combinations of parts that are not, in themselves, new. It is conceivable, therefore, that almost all mechanical patent applications could be rejected by hypothetical reference.

But don't let this worry you too much. Most applications do result in patent. Obviously then the patent examiners use the hypothetical reference with discretion, and only when they really do think that the combination of parts is pretty obvious.

● preparation of the amendments

Your patent application is now back on your attorney's desk. His next task is to study the nature of the examiner's objections to your claims. "Fully met," "Lack of novelty," "Unpatentable over (*such and such a patent*)"—these will be some of the phrases that confront him. As he studies them, he refers to the various patents the examiner has cited. Of course, he'll take you into his confidence, and suggest that you read these patents too. They'll give you a knowledge of the prior art that you didn't have before, and may well give both you and your attorney a new slant on **just what is different** about your invention.

This is a point at which having a good, experienced attorney is of vital importance. His judgment has to be sound. If the examiner's objections to your claims are so clearly right and true that it seems highly unlikely that you will be able to get a patent, it can be that your case is hopeless. If your attorney now counsels you to abandon the attempt to get a patent, you'd do well to heed his advice.

In most cases, however, he's unlikely to be disturbed by what the examiner says, and will proceed to the business of preparing the "first amendment" to your application. This must be filed within six months of receipt of the first letter from the examiner. You and your attorney may well need the whole six months to work out a new set of claims.

Here's how the Patent Office spells out your task:

> In order to be entitled to a reexamination or reconsideration, the applicant must make a request therefor in writing, and he must distinctly and specifically point out the supposed errors in the examiner's action; the applicant must respond to every ground of objection and rejection . . . the mere allegation that the examiner has erred will not be received as a proper reason for such reexamination or reconsideration.

In this first amendment, your attorney will delete claims that cannot be sustained in view of the examiner's grounds for rejection, and he will change such claims that seem sustainable with deletions or additions of words, phrases or sentences.

He will draft and enter such new claims as seem advisable in light of the prior art the examiner has disclosed. But these new claims, if any, must relate to structures detailed in the original application. No new matter may be included in them.

If you have thought of some improvements for your structure in the interim between application and this amendment, you must file a new patent application covering these improvements if you wish to protect them with patent.

Your attorney will attempt to answer the examiner's every reason for rejection with a counter-argument, which, he hopes, will demolish the examiner's objection.

The examiner will consider the amended application, again going over every claim. He may still reject many, but this time there are more likely to be some he will allow. However, much to your dismay, he may even now search out and use as a reference some hitherto unmentioned patent.

When through with his consideration he will send your attorney the "second official action," to which you again have six months to reply.

And so it goes, through maybe as many as half a dozen amendments to your original application, until you either have a patent or a final rejection.

If your patent has been refused you can either accept the examiner's decision or appeal.

● appeal of a rejected patent application or claim

If the examiner rejects your application or makes a final rejection of a given claim (two rejections of the same claim usually constitute final rejection), he has said his last word as far as he is concerned. There is no more arguing with him.

But, if you want to go to the trouble and expense of carrying the matter further, you can appeal.

If you are considering appeal, your attorney is, of course, the man with whom you should consult. He will give you a realistic appraisal of your chances of success—which, statistically, are not very good—and a realistic appraisal of the cost of appeal, which will be considerable. You can then weigh your chances and the cost against the financial returns you could get if your appeal is successful.

An appeal is taken first to the Board of Appeals, which is a body of 14 men working for the Patent Office. They are appointed by the President of the U.S. and their appointments are approved by the Senate.

The fee for appeal to this board is $25, but in appeal cases you also have additional attorney's fees, of course, which can be many times that amount.

Appeal to the Board of Appeals must be made within six months of the examiner's rejection. If not taken within that time, your invention is considered to be abandoned. In fact, this is the case throughout this succession of rejections and amendments. After each communication you are given six months in which to reply, and if you should ever fail to do so, your invention is considered abandoned. Such an invention passes into the public domain.

If you do appeal, this is what happens:

Your attorney files a "brief" with the Board and lists the references, authorities, and arguments he will use in pleading your case, and presents a concise description of your invention and the claim or claims in question.

Within four months after your attorney files this brief, the examiner will give the Board a written answer to it, again giving fully his reasons for rejection of any of the claims. A copy of this statement will be sent to your attorney.

You can request either an oral hearing, or a hearing "on brief," which simply means that the Board will make its decision on the basis of your attorney's brief and the examiner's written statement, without a personal appearance on the part of your attorney. (The examiner will not appear personally in either case.)

The Board may uphold the examiner's decision in its entirety, reverse it in its entirety, or reverse it in part.

If you are rejected by the Board, you're still not beaten. You may take your appeal out of the Patent Office and into court, either the Court of Customs and Patent Appeals, or the District Court of the District of Columbia.

Which of these courts you appeal to makes quite a bit of difference, and the one you choose will depend entirely on the nature of your case.

The Court of Customs and Patent Appeals will only review the record of your application, together with any facts presented by the Patent Office, and your arguments as to why the examiner and the Board of Appeals have been wrong in denying you a patent.

The fee for this appeal is only $15, but there is further cost in providing the court with printed copies of the Patent Office records and your brief. And again you will have to pay the costs of retaining your attorney to represent you. An appeal through this court takes about two years.

If, on the other hand, you take your appeal to the District Court, you are not limited to a review of the Patent Office history of your application. In this court you may present new evidence, including witnesses or a working model of your invention, that may prove, in your estimation, its novelty. An appeal to this court is a civil matter and therefore takes the form of a suit against the Commissioner of Patents, who will be legally represented in court.

All in all, appeal of any kind is a costly, troublesome business, and you are advised to undertake it only when you are convinced that you really have a strong case and are certain that your patent, if obtained, will be profitable enough to warrant the expenditure of money and effort.

● interference

With nearly 2,000 applications for patent received every week, and the resulting backload of a quarter of a million patents pending, it is not surprising that sometimes the Patent

Office finds that one or more inventors are simultaneously seeking to patent identical or very similar inventions.

When such a situation is discovered by the Patent Office, an "interference" results. This proceeding is designed to answer the question: **Who is the first inventor?**

The first step the Patent Office takes is to write letters to the inventors, asking them to write the claims from the other inventor's application into their own applications. This is done so that the applications are identical. Then the whole question of who gets the patent boils down to who was the first man to invent the structure in question. If one or both want to claim that the applications do not, in fact, conflict, there is a time for such a claim later.

Sometimes it happens that the Patent Office will miss conflicting applications, and grant conflicting patents. After all, patent examiners are human. In such a case the Patent Office cannot by itself call an interference, but either patentee may apply for a "reissue" of his patent within one year of the issuance date of the other patent. This will bring about an interference.

Only the person with the patent that was issued second can gain anything from this procedure, for where two patents are issued on the same matter, the patent with the earliest filing date is automatically dominant over any later patent.

When an interference has been declared, each party to it must file a preliminary statement, under oath. This statement must tell: (1) if the invention was made in the U.S., (2) the date of the first drawing of the invention, (3) the date of the first disclosure to an outside person, (4) the provable date of the invention's conception, (5) the date the invention was "reduced to practice," (6) the date when the inventor began working more or less steadily on the invention if this date is not identical with the date of conception, (7) the filing dates of any corresponding foreign patent applications either issued or in the works, (8) the numbers and titles of any other U.S. patents previously issued to the inventor or any co-pending applications. Any date you give in this preliminary statement must stand. You cannot later make an attempt to prove an earlier date.

This preliminary statement is testimony in a legal proceeding, and giving false information in it constitutes perjury.

When the preliminary statements are filed and have been approved by the Examiner of Interferences, the inventors are allowed to obtain copies of their opponent's preliminary statement and application file from the Patent Office.

After the filing of the preliminary statements, there ensues a 30-day "motion period," when either inventor's attorney may take any of a number of subtle legal steps—to dissolve the interference; to claim that the applications don't conflict; to say that there is no interference because the claims of the applications, as they stand, are not allowable anyway; to bring other applications into the interference; to claim that there is a flaw in the other inventor's application; etc.

If you were involved in an interference case, you would probably, during this motion period, be staying awake nights trying to decide on the best course of action. Carrying an interference proceeding to the bitter end can be a very costly process (the tab may run to thousands of dollars).

If it looks like your chances of winning the case are considerably less than half, you should give up, of course. Even if you have a good chance, it is possible that you can spend more money fighting the case than your patent could ever make for you—if you win.

There is always the possibility of compromise. Either you or your opponent can agree to write an "abandonment," or a concession of priority, in return for a contracted sum of money or a percentage of any returns on the invention. If you don't have an open-and-shut case, have your attorney explore the possibilities of compromise with the rival inventor. It's certainly cheaper, and it can save a lot of grief.

● if you decide to fight it out

However, maybe you feel you have such a strong case, and such a valuable invention, that you want to fight it out. In such a case, here's what would happen next:

Parties to the interference, along with their attorneys and witnesses, assemble somewhere, usually in the office of one of the attorneys, and make sworn statements relevant to the question of who was the first inventor. This whole proceeding is transcribed and must be witnessed by a notary public or other legally authorized person. The transcription is sent to the Examiner of Interferences.

Then your attorney submits his brief to the examiner, as does the opposing attorney, and a date is set for the attorneys to appear in Washington before the Board of Interferences, at which time, on the basis of the preliminary statements, the testimony, and the lawyers' arguments, the interference is decided.

● the day you get your patent

But let's turn away from this discussion of the trouble you can get into in the patenting process to a more cheerful side of things.

The odds are in favor of your getting your patent, with or without such travail as an interference proceeding. (It's a relatively rare occurrence.) So probably one day you will receive notification from the Patent Office that your application has been allowed.

Of course, there's still one piece of unfinished business—the payment of a fee (what else?). This one is for $30 and must be paid within six months of notification. With what you've spent by this time, the fact that this payment is known as "the final fee" is bound to make you let out a sigh of relief.

Then one proud day you receive in the mail your genuine U.S. patent, a handsome, beribboned document that tells the world what you have invented.

Where do you stand now? There are two schools of thought among inventors on this question. The optimist holds that now he has it made. His patent seems, to him, an irrevocable guarantee of control over his invention and an assurance that he will get rich. The pessimist holds that there is still nothing but trouble ahead. Someone will try to invalidate his patent, nobody will buy his invention, and everybody will do everything he can to keep him from making a nickel.

The truth, of course, lies somewhere between these two poles of opinion. The pessimists are right in that bad things can happen. Yes, it is possible that a patent can be invalidated after issuance. The examiner may have made a mistake; the attorney may have made a mistake. But such occurrences are really very rare, and it's time enough to worry about it if it happens. Yes, you might have trouble making money with your invention. You might even go broke. But that's the way the American free-enterprise system works.

The optimists have truth on their side too. In general, patents are valid. They do protect against infringement and give you the right to "exclude others from making, selling or using" your invention. A sizeable percentage of patented inventions do make money for their creators, sometimes a little, sometimes a lot.

It is to the subject of making money with your invention that we turn in the succeeding chapters of this book. We don't have to wish you luck, because if you have a good invention, a good patent, and if you go about it in the right ways, you will get the financial return your inventive effort deserves.

finding a prospect
for your invention

There comes a day in the life of the inventor when he must face up to the baffling question of who's going to make and sell his invention. Who is going to pay him all those dollars in royalties that he feels should roll into his pockets when the public gets a chance to buy the manufactured product of his inventive skill?

For the inventor, the better mouse trap maxim just doesn't apply. No manufacturer is going to come to you, no matter how promising your invention. Somehow, you must find a firm that can be interested in it. We've known many situations where, for various reasons, just one company in the country had a compelling motivation for buying a particular invention at a particular time.

● what to offer a big company

There is a widespread view that America's big corporations never buy outside inventions. After all, why should a company with hundreds of inventors on its research and development payroll find it necessary to go outside its organization? Equally widespread is the view that these corporations are eager to buy, not only outside inventions, but simply ideas for inventions—and pay fabulous prices for them to boot.

Both views are wrong. Big corporations *do* buy outside inventions, but not many, and rarely for enormous sums. GE, IBM, DuPont, Lever Bros., 3 M, Westinghouse, and Aluminum Company of America, are just a few of the blue-chip outfits which have, on occasion, purchased inventions from freelancers.

What makes big business buy the inventions that it does? To find the answer, examine the stories of some inventors who have sold inventions to big companies.

When Leonard Marrafino, a Mount Vernon, N.Y., printer, and John Spero, a draftsman, joined forces to devise a means of putting a stripe in toothpaste, they came up with a small plastic gadget that goes in the top of the tube. When the tube is squeezed, coloring matter comes through slots, making stripes.

Here, they knew, was an invention that had to be sold to a big pharmaceutical firm, for the sale of toothpaste is dominated by the giants that have the distribution and advertising budgets needed to market such a heavily promoted, competitive product.

Yet competition was just the factor that enabled the inventors to sell their device to Lever Bros. Here was something that clearly would give the purchasing company a competitive advantage. In fact, the inventors discovered that several pharmaceutical firms had worked, unsuccessfully, to find a way of doing what their device did so handily. It "sold itself" to Lever Bros., who used it to make their *Stripe* toothpaste.

When George Breen invented his *Mapleflo*, the system of plastic tubes he devised for tapping maple trees, he turned to big Minnesota Mining and Manufacturing, the company from which he had acquired the tubing for his original model on his Vermont farm. While *Mapleflo* is a specialty item, limited in its market to a few thousand farmers who own a "sugarbush," any one installation uses a lot of tubing. Breen used 20 miles of it on his farm. To 3 M it was a logical purchase because it offered an expanded market for a product it already made.

James Robbins, who invented the first successful coin-operated dry cleaning machine (see Chapter 1), knew from the beginning that only a big appliance maker could profit from his invention. While he was working on his machine, he was learning all he could about the situations of various appliance makers. Which companies were already geared to launch coin-operated dry cleaning franchises? He picked four, and the second one to which the invention was offered, Norge, bought it.

A Dayton, Ohio, engineer, Ermal C. Frase, who devised a way to open a beer can by pulling a tab, knew that the company to buy it would be a can maker, or the maker of materials that went into the cans. Frase picked mighty Aluminum Company of America as his logical prospect. It was a good bet, because Alcoa bought it, licensing its use to can makers who use the company's product. Frase contentedly collects a royalty on every can.

The common denominator in these sales (and in every other such sale we've checked) to big "impossible-to-sell-to" firms is this: **The outside inventions they bought could increase their business or improve their competitive position.** They were all "big" inventions in the sales sense. The research-oriented corporations are all notably cool to minor, gadget-type innovations and devices which simply offer some slight improvement on or variation in their products.

Thus, an inventor who approached the big appliance makers with a detergent dispenser for attachment to washing machines got no place. In fact, he probably shouldn't have gone to the expense of getting a patent at all, since his preliminary search had revealed some patents for devices which accomplished the same purpose—patents held by firms which would be his only possible customers.

Neither did the inventor of a special tire tread get a favorable reception from any big tire and rubber company. His scheme was good, and perfectly workable, but it really would have brought about only a slight improvement, not one that would increase any company's business. The companies' own R & D people, though they had not come up with exactly this invention, had developed many other tread designs that, for marketing purposes, were just as good.

Of course, there's no getting around the fact that, no matter how promising your invention, the greatest obstacle to its sale to a big corporation is what's going on in its own R & D set up. Nonetheless, if your invention is the kind that must be, or would best be, handled by a large company, you should go ahead and offer it.

Fortunately for the inventor, all major concerns have set up procedures for considering outside inventions. Though the company may have given a special name, like GE's "Submitted Ideas," to the particular department dealing with outside inventions, you need know no more than the name and address of the company to which you're offering your invention. "Patent Department" is a possible addition you might make.

• how to find a small company prospect for your invention

Most inventions offered to big corporations should have been offered to small, specialized concerns instead. Inventors present them to the big outfits simply because they are easy-to-spot targets, not because they are logical prospects. There are, it is safe to say, literally thousands of inventions not on the market today simply because the inventors have not succeeded in finding the right companies to make them.

The sad part of it is that this "right company" may sorely need just the invention that was never brought to its attention. Many concerns of moderate size have a real problem finding enough products to make and sell. They have down time on their machines and sales facilities that could just as well handle another item.

Dr. Robert Horton's sale of his *Slumbertone*, the transistorized buzzer device that lulls babies to sleep, is a fine example of a small company natural. The Trundle Bundle Company, of Duluth, Minnesota, was already distributing the Trundle Bundle, a bag-type sleeping garment for infants. The *Slumbertone* device, going to exactly the same retail outlets—department stores and infants' wear shops—fitted in perfectly with the company's sales facilities.

The invention of Mike Remeika, of Madison, Wsiconsin, is another case of a device inherently suited for handling by a smaller company. Remeika, as described in Chapter 2, developed a way to impregnate corn cob pipes with a detergent solution. This made them into remarkable bubble pipes that could blow bubbles without the use of any special solution. The company which bought it, Jak-Pak, Inc., of Milwaukee, specialized in novelty items which it sold to cereal companies as premiums. Remeika's bubble pipe, an inexpensive item, was ideally suited for this purpose.

But how do you find the right small company? If it's even hard for a broker who's in the business, how on earth can the lone inventor reach the likely prospects?

We advise any inventor to begin his search locally. Go to the secretary of your Chamber of Commerce. He'll have a list of all local manufacturers and know their situations. If there's any possibility that one of them might be a market for your invention, he'll be able to tell you. Moreover, he will call the company for you and give you a proper send-off. We know of a case where an inventor sold his invention to a firm a thousand miles from home when, right in his own community, there was a company which was actually looking for new products just like the boat bailer he had invented.

If no local firm expresses an interest, there are various ways to obtain lists of firms which might be prospects. One of the best is to look in stores and other outlets where similar products are sold and see who makes them. Look for items having the same general construction your invention has. A company manufacturing a product with a plastic housing may be a good bet for an invention which also uses a plastic housing, though one of a quite different shape, different purpose and different plastic. Here is at least an indication that the firm is capable of making and distributing that sort of thing.

Look at the trade journals for advertisements. In them you'll see ads for many items that you won't find in any one store. Ads sometimes tell you a lot about a company because in them it will often list other products it makes and indicate its sales record with them. These ads are right on the beam for you as an inventor, because they are actually appeals to stores and users to stock or purchase somebody else's invention. You can size up the possibilities of your own invention fitting into the company's line by the type of advertising appeal it makes.

A third method of finding a specialized company that might make your invention is the shotgun technique. You simply mail out a number of letters, stating that you have such and such an invention, and outlining its purpose and points of superiority. In it you ask, "Would you be interested in seeing the patent (or patent application) of this invention?" You won't get too many bites, but from a sizeable mailing of, say, a hundred or more, you can expect a few.

You can get the names of firms in the field of making any particular items from *Thomas' Register,* which lists all companies in the U.S. under headings indicating the products they make. It also will give you the size of the company. You can view *Thomas' Register* at your public library. Or, if your local library doesn't have it, see if you can consult a copy at a nearby manufacturing plant.

There is another source of specific information about firms

which might be interested in your invention. That is the Small Business Administration of the U.S. Dept. of Commerce. A personal visit to a regional office, or a letter to this office, may result in a suggestion from a SBA official about possible prospects. For a list of such offices, see the *Inventor's Reference Guide*.

Is it possible to get interested companies to come to you? Not usually. Classified advertisements in big newspapers have been placed by some inventors, but most of them report disappointing results. However, we know of one instance in which the inventor of a pharmaceutical product did find a $150,000 buyer in this manner.

You can also advertise in a government publication. For a fee of $3 the Patent Office will list your invention in the *Official Gazette* in a section entitled "Patents Available for Licensing and Sale."

Even if you do not list it there, your invention is, of course, described in the *Gazette* at the time you get your patent, and will therefore be brought to the attention of firms which subscribe to the *Gazette* and keep an eye on new patents. The Small Business Administration puts out a *Products List Circular*, in which it runs descriptions of some of the promising inventions brought to its attention.

While these methods of notifying buyers that you have an invention for sale are worth trying, we must in all candor advise the inventor not to have any hopes that his invention will "sell itself." On the other hand, beware of the blandishments of the "invention shark" who sets your heart to beating faster by a letter announcing he "has a buyer" for your invention at some wondrously high price. We'll have more to say about this in Chapter 12.

the terms of sale

After you have lined up what you consider likely prospects, be they small or big, you are still confronted with twin problems: On what terms will they consider your invention? And on what terms will you sell it to them?

● offering the unpatented invention for sale

Many inventors ask these questions: Can I offer my invention to a manufacturer before I apply for a patent? Will manufacturers consider such inventions? Is it safe to offer an invention on which I haven't even applied for a patent?

The answer to all three questions is in the affirmative—but with some qualifications. Inventions *are* offered and sold before patenting. Major Jack Dixon, the inventor of *Pitch Back*, did it that way. He wasn't sure he even had a patentable invention, and he didn't want to go to the expense of seeking a patent at the time he developed the first model of his baseball-returning device. All he had to send the manufacturer was a crude model, made of 2 x 2's and strips of inner tube rubber. Still he was able to sell it. The purchaser took over the whole burden of obtaining the patent and paid Dixon a comfortable royalty.

This manufacturer was not exceptional, although it is true that some firms are more reluctant than others about considering unpatented inventions and that some will not consider them at all.

Most manufacturers, however, have a policy which states that the inventor will rely solely on the patent rights obtainable for his invention. This means simply that if your invention is not patentable at all the company may use it without paying you anything, or at most a nominal "finder's fee." But if it is patentable, that's different again, and some manufacturers, if they like the invention enough, may even pay the expenses involved in doing the patent work for you.

Kessler Sales Corporation has asked the question of many manufacturers as to whether they will consider unpatented inventions. Most agree that an invention that is unpatented when they first see it may have as much value to them as one that is patented. But note the difference between an invention which is unpatented but patentable, and one which is not patentable at all. Inventors who wish to try selling their inventions before laying out the costs of doing all the patent work should at least have a search made to determine if their invention does have patentability.

General Electric, in offering instructions to persons submitting inventions on such a basis, explains that the inventor "may make a written description and sketches of the idea, signing and dating both the description and the sketches. These should be made in duplicate, one of the duplicates being submitted to us while the other is retained for his own record. In order that he may be in a better position to prove the making of any such written description or sketch, he should consider disclosure to some person or persons who can understand the idea and who will sign and date both duplicates as a witness.

" .... it is not necessary for consideration by the Company that artistic drawings be prepared; rough sketches are sufficient. Nor is it necessary that any particular phraseology be employed in the description. It is important only that the description supplemented by the sketches shall disclose the idea so clearly that a person ordinarily skilled in the technical field to which it relates can understand just what the submitter proposes to do and how he proposes to do it. It will be helpful if the submitter will point out what he believes to be new and set forth some of the advantages which he thinks the idea has over known devices or processes.

"If a technical idea seems to be of interest and patentable, negotiations can be started for the purchase of rights with respect to the patent or patent application involved, if any has been filed, or for the purchase of rights with respect to a patent application eventually to be filed, if this action has not already been taken."

While these suggestions are those of one firm, they are applicable to the offering of unpatented inventions to other companies. Kessler Sales Corporation, acting as sales representative for inventors, provides them with a PROOF OF INVENTION form. In it the inventor provides drawings and a written description of his invention, both of which are to be witnessed and dated.

The question of possible theft of an inventive idea is one that often comes up in the inventor's mind. Isn't your unpatented invention likely to be appropriated by a company to which you offer it? We don't think so. Kessler Sales Corporation has dealt with literally hundreds of companies over a long period of years and has yet to encounter a single case in which an invention was "stolen" by a manufacturer.

The greatest danger in submitting an unpatented invention isn't that it will be stolen so much as it is that the company won't see fit to pay very much for it. The low price tag is evidenced by the Westinghouse statement of policy:

"We do not agree to the payment of any compensation for the adoption and use of unpatented ideas; except that if we use the idea in substantially the form submitted, if it was new to us, and its use is of material benefit to us, we will consider payment in accordance with its reasonable value, up to a maximum of $1,500."

DuPont puts it this way: "DuPont is under no obligation to make a payment to the inventor, and in the absence of a patent, the inventor must be willing to rely completely upon DuPont's judgment as to the value of the suggestion and the amount of compensation to be paid to the inventor."

● selling the patent-applied-for invention

From the inventor's standpoint it's obviously an advantage to get things moving during the three years or so that are bound to elapse between the time you apply for your patent and the day you actually get it. And from the standpoint of the company which may purchase it, timeliness may be enough of a factor to make the company as eager to get going as the inventor.

James Robbins' coin-operated dry cleaning machine, which revolutionized an industry, was sold to the manufacturer before his patent came through. So, too, was Ermal Frase's pull-top beer can opener. Look at many new gadgets in stores and you'll see a surprising number that bear the words "Patent Pending."

There have been cases where a small fortune has been earned before the patent was issued. A good illustration is the story of Sanford Redmond's butter slicer. The machine developed by this New York inventor cuts a portion of butter, places it on a coated paper, and covers it with a greaseproof paper lid. Used by restaurants, airlines, hospitals, schools, it was on the market and in such wide use that it was cutting half the butter pats used in the U.S. before the patent was finally issued.

In offering for sale an invention on which you have applied for a patent, the common procedure is to accompany it with (1) a statement that you have applied for a patent, and (2) a photostatic copy of the patent application, including, of course, the drawings.

You do *not* include any indication of the date on which you filed your patent application, nor the file number you were assigned by the Patent Office at the time you made your application.

Companies feel more comfortable not having this information. Without it, they cannot be accused of trying to fabricate records and suborn witnesses in an attempt to indicate that its researchers were already at work on just such an invention.

• can you set the price in advance?

In negotiating the sale of unpatented or patent-applied-for inventions, the problem of "full disclosure" arises. Indeed, it can come up on patented inventions too. Many an inventor has the mistaken idea that he can negotiate with a company about a possible purchase of his invention, putting a price tag on it before he tells them what it's all about.

Typically, the inventor says something like this to the company, "I have an invention that will do thus and so. I'll tell you all about it and give you a description of it (or a demonstration of it) or show you my patent on it, *after* you agree to pay me X number of dollars. That is, if you buy it when I prove that it does what I say it will do."

To the inventor this may seem reasonable, but not to the company. We've never heard of a firm that would agree to a fixed price in advance of "full disclosure," as it's called. What the company will pay is not so casually decided. A company has to know a lot about an invention before it can decide just what it's worth to them. And that's often a lot less than the inventor thinks it's worth!

● royalties

The standard method of sale of an invention, and the one that appeals most to inventors, is to permit manufacture by a company or companies which pay a royalty, that is, a percentage or fixed monetary sum on every item manufactured and sold.

The figure set for the royalty varies greatly. Many inventors have an exaggerated idea of how royalties usually run. We've heard inventors announce that they expect royalties running as high as 25% of retail price. We've never heard of any company granting anything like that, for it is simply an economic impossibility for any concern to do it.

On high-volume, low-profit items in a retail bracket of 25¢ to $1.00, a 2% royalty on the net selling price (the price the manufacturer sells for) is, as a rule, about what may be expected. On a certain item selling in the stores for 98¢, the manufacturer received 48¢, the inventor about 1¢. Thus, on a sale of 2,000,000 units in one year, the inventor received $20,000 —not a fortune, certainly, but a pretty comfortable return on what seems an extremely low royalty. It must be remembered that on items of this kind, the manufacturer's profit is also reckoned in very small percentages. The inventor of a toothbrush sold to a large company received a royalty of ⅓¢ per brush.

Items selling for more than $1 but under $5 bring, as a rule, a somewhat higher royalty—3% and 4% being quite common. On higher priced products there can be an enormous variation, depending on the type of device involved. Percentages can be higher—as much as 10% on some items—but they can also be lower. To show you how these royalties can vary, take the case of a device selling in the infant departments of department stores for $10.95. In this case, the inventor received a royalty of 65¢ a unit—about 10% of the net selling price. This was on a non-competitive novelty item. The inventor of a boat attachment, retailing at about the same price as the item above, was paid 40¢ a unit.

Many variations are possible. Some contracts are arranged to pay the inventor a smaller percentage in the first year in recognition of the manufacturer's higher costs during the tooling up period. On one such deal, for example, on a machine selling at $495, the royalty the first year was 5%, jumping to 7½% the second year and all years thereafter.

Royalty payments are often coupled with a down payment made at the time the contract is signed. This may be either a flat payment or an advance against royalties. Here, too, there is an enormous variation. We have seen cases where this down payment amounted to only a nominal $250, and others in which it has run very high. One inventor of an electrical instrument was paid $40,000 at the time his contract was signed. This is exceptional, and usually payments on royalty contracts run rather small—disappointingly small to many inventors.

Royalties are paid at the end of a specified accounting period. Some contracts call for monthly accounting and payment, but quarterly and semi-annual payments are more common. Many call for a specified minimum payment, regardless of sales during a given period. Generally these payments are based on the manufacturer's guarantee to produce the invention in at least a certain quantity.

● outright sale

Attractive as royalty sales may be to the inventor, there are situations in which a flat payment fits the situation better. This applies particularly in cases of machines or devices which are to become part of another piece of equipment. A food processing machinery company recently paid $35,000 outright for an instrument that would be built into certain of its equipment. A royalty would have been inappropriate because it would have been hard to establish the relationship of the instrument to increased sales in the machines. The company would not even have considered paying a percentage.

Of course, inventions are sometimes sold outright for very small sums, and one hears many tales of the inventor being "robbed." Now it is true that one of the best selling toys of all time was sold for $800 outright. And it is true that many an inventor has been offered what seemed like a ridiculously small sum. We know of an instance in which $1,000 was the top price offered for a household device. However, the circumstances were such that this is about all it was worth. The patent claims were so limited that the invention was not of much value to the company. And this was the only company which had any interest in the invention. We must say that, within our observation, "robbery" has never been the motive for a low offer of outright purchase.

a broker to help you sell

Should you use the services of a broker to sell your invention? First, let's clear up a lot of confusion about just what a broker is and does.

A broker should be thought of as a *sales representative*. He has, essentially, three jobs:

• 1 • He finds prospects who might be interested in producing and selling your invention.

• 2 • He presents your invention for their consideration.

• 3 • He handles the actual sales negotiations.

Whether you need a broker or not depends on how well set up you are to perform all three of these jobs without one. Since one of us (Kessler) *is* an invention broker, we might be accused of bias in saying that very few inventors are able to carry out all three. Many inventors do so, of course, and with success—as we have pointed out in many other sections of this book.

However, we feel that, if they were in the shoes of the invention broker, even inventors who don't think they need one would share the sentiments of one client of Kessler Sales Corporation, who, upon being presented with a list of the many activities being carried out on his behalf, shook his head and said fervently, "Whew! I'm glad *you're* the ones doing it." In view of all the problems which even the broker, for all his experience, runs into, we take off our hats to the hardy inventor who does succeed in do-it-yourself selling of his invention.

• how to choose a broker

It is on the basis of his ability to carry out the task of acting as sales representative that you should choose a broker. Unfortunately, the inventor may have some difficulty judging the capabilities and honesty of the brokers who proffer their services. The U.S. Patent Office exercises no control over brokers. There is no professional society which sets up any standards. It's up to the inventor to check. Fortunately, there are some standards of measurement by which you can judge a broker.

• 1 • Beware of one who offers too much. If he is a jack-of-all-trades who will "help you get a patent," "analyze and evaluate you invention," and even "aid you in its commercial development," he is quite probably preparing you for his demand of a fee far in excess of what a legitimate broker charges for his *sales* services. Even if he is completely honest, such a broker may be so busy with activities other than selling that he can't do a job for your invention.

• 2 • Beware of the broker who puts a fancy price tag on your invention the moment he hears of it, using some such phrase as "This invention is so impressive that I would not hesitate to ask for a large down payment and $10,000 (or $20,000) a year guaranteed payment." A legitimate broker knows that it is impossible to put a price tag on an invention in advance of putting it on the market.

• 3 • Beware of the broker who cannot present notarized letters from satisfied inventors who have used his services.

• 4 • Beware of the broker who does not present meaningful local references, such as banks and the Chamber of Commerce.

We suggest that one of the best investments an inventor can make is the modest fee his own personal attorney will charge for investigating any brokers he is considering. A letter written by your attorney should request: (1) notarized letters from at least five satisfied clients, (2) a list of local references, (3) a copy of the contract the broker wishes to make with the inventor.

The phonies are unlikely to reply at all. The legitimate ones will do so promptly because they are not afraid of scrutiny and know that an inventor who has engaged an attorney to investigate brokers means business. With the various replies and check-ups on references on his desk, your attorney will be able to help you pick a dependable broker who will give your invention the break it deserves.

● what does a broker charge?

There is wide misunderstanding about what a broker charges and why. All invention brokers charge a fee, plus a commission. Some refund the fee if the invention is sold.

Inventors have no difficulty in understanding the commission, but many, unfamiliar with the problems of selling an invention, raise a question of why this fee, generally less than $100, is necessary. We can perhaps best explain it by quoting from the literature of Kessler Sales Corporation:

"The operations of an invention broker are not like the operations of, say, a real estate broker. The real estate broker can appraise the property listed with him, but this is denied us because inventions cannot be appraised in advance. They must first be tested on the manufacturers. So just as a patent attorney makes a patent search to determine if an invention is patentable, we make a 'commercial search' to determine if the manufacturers believe it has commercial value. The fee we charge is to cover the work of submitting the invention to the manufacturers. Our commission applies if through our efforts a manufacturer ultimately buys or licenses the invention.

"The fee covers: (1) The preparation of the sales and descriptive matter for submittal to the manufacturers to determine their interest. (2) The selection of the manufacturers who might be prospects for the invention. (3) The submission of the sales material to these manufacturers. (4) Carrying on all necessary correspondence with any manufacturers denoting interest. (5) Answering their questions, forwarding models at their request, consulting with the inventor as required to furnish manufacturer any information he wants, etc.

"Included in our costs for this service are salaries of our staff, overhead, telephone and telegraph bills, preparation of sales materials and folios, printing, duplication and photocopying of drawings and specifications, postage, etc.

"So you can see why our fee is necessary and why we could not possibly maintain the organization we do, the preparation we make, without charging our fee. Quite frequently inventors write us to ask if we will not dispense with the fee and the foregoing explanation covers the reasons why we cannot. Secondly, it would not be fair to charge one inventor and not another. You, in paying our fee, would certainly not approve of any policy wherein we did not charge the same fee to another inventor."

The commission charged by brokers varies. However, ordinarily 10% of the inventor's receipts seems fair. A lower commission may not give the broker adequate incentive toward making a sale. On the other hand, a higher one may take away too much of the rightful earnings of a successful invention.

Let's take a look at the way a broker carries out his three functions.

● the prospect list

This is the real heart and soul of an invention sales representative's operation. There are some 50,000 manufacturers of one sort and another in the U.S. Some of them want inventions, some don't. Some are truly eager to consider them; some are only reluctantly willing. Some will consider inventions in a wide range; others want very specific ones of a highly specialized nature. Moreover, these needs are in a constant state of change.

Companies which were once active markets can suddenly cease to be active, for any one of a number of reasons. Perhaps they have gone into the manufacture of other products and no longer want to consider inventions; or maybe their market situation has changed, or their management. On the other hand, companies which formerly had no interest in buying inventions can become favorably inclined toward doing so as their situations change.

So the broker finds himself faced with the problem of keeping tabs on a vast, volatile invention market. Here is where the inventor must be wary of the shady operators who infest the field. These operators make no real effort to compile and keep up to date a list of real prospects. They just take a list of manufacturers and use it for every kind of invention, year after year. They make the boast, "We offer your invention to 1000 companies!" and this may be technically true. But how ridiculous it is to label a big electric company, let us say, a prospect for a toy, or a toy company a prospect for a new kind of oil burner. Yet just such ludicrous offerings are made.

The only way in which a broker can keep up a really active prospect list is to keep working at it. Kessler Sales Corporation maintains an extensive Library of Manufacturers, and employs a librarian and staff who do nothing but contact companies to determine their current requirements in inventions. This is done by a continuous questionnaire.

"Would be interested in seeing roller bearing devices." "Our greatest need is metal products that can be machined on ——————— type machines." "Seek product which can be made on our new extrusion machines." "Adding to our sales force—need items similar to our successful ———————."

These are some typical favorable comments that come back.

Of course, they're balanced off by some typical unfavorable ones: "Never consider outside inventions." "All our facilities in use—want no new products." "Changing to contract manufacture."

This winnowing process brings the number of real prospects down considerably—generally to less than a hundred for any given invention. But the point is that they are genuine prospects that the brokerage firm would not have known about had it not made the special, continuing effort to determine the requirements of possible purchasers.

The question the inventor must ask himself is whether he is in a position to do the type of checking necessary to sift out the few actual prospects. You can, of course, do it by mass mailings. You can also, as we have pointed out earlier, do some selection by studying what companies make what products. We're pretty sure, however, that the process of getting a list of prospects will cost the inventor more if he does it himself than if he turns the task over to a completely reliable broker for whom such lists are part of his stock in trade.

Since making a sale, or not making one, is often a matter of timing, the fact that a broker has prospect information in his files can be of crucial importance. Look at a case in which an inventor came to Kessler Sales Corporation with a highly specialized invention—a utility post-hole digger to attach to motorized equipment. The files indicated that there were no more than 20 companies which would be even remotely interested in such an invention. And, when they were contacted, only one of them expressed any active interest. This particular firm had just gotten a contract to equip trucks for use in undeveloped countries. It had indicated its need for truck attachments to the brokerage firm and, when the broker offered the invention to them, they bought it.

• submitting the invention

The broker's second big job is submitting the invention to the live prospects he's rounded up. Rarely does he do this in person. First of all, many of the prospects are distant. Also, at preliminary stages of discussion, most concerns prefer to study written descriptions and drawings of inventions.

These written descriptions, as handled by Kessler and other reputable brokers, are relatively brief. The documentary packet presented to a prospect consists of a carefully worked out description of the invention; a summary of its possible commercial merits; a copy of the patent or the patent application; the drawings on the patent or the application, or explanatory drawings similar to these.

A wise broker resists the temptation that often hurts the inventor in making his own submission—the tendency to send too much. At the early stages of the game, a mass of material about the invention surely doesn't help its sale. The executive who gets it is all too likely to shove it aside because he is too busy to wade through it all. Nor is any executive going to respond to high-pressure sales letters.

The Kessler system is to offer just enough. As a Kessler booklet puts it: "We try to make it easy for them to take the next step of asking for more information or contacting us again. We always state, 'Write us or call us collect for any further information you desire.' Usually they write, but frequently they call."

The brokerage firm, with its facilities for duplicating materials, can obviously produce the essential literature more cheaply than the individual inventor should he engage a letter shop to do the work. Many inventors who have sent out copies of their patents, obtained at 25¢ apiece from the Patent Office, have found their total cost per offering running above 50¢.

• negotiating the sale

However, valuable as the broker's services described thus far may be, the individual inventor *can* get along without them. He may make mistakes, he may end up paying out more than the broker's fee would have cost him, he quite probably won't do it all as well as the professional broker can; but he can do it.

The authors doubt, however, that the inventor can successfully carry out the third function of the broker—the complicated one of negotiating a sale. Most of the time, when and if an inventor does reach this point, he realizes he has to bring in a third party, for suddenly he finds himself facing demands on his time, capabilities, and finances that he's simply unable to meet.

Perhaps the best way to see what is involved in selling an invention is to look at the negotiating effort and expense that went into a typical broker-negotiated sale:

> May 10. Long distance call from interested firm 500 miles from broker's office (farther than that from the inventor's town). Fifteen minute discussion with V.P. about sales possibilities of invention.

> May 12. Second call. This time from the production manager of company. Can the broker give him some more figures on the production costs the inventor had obtained from local companies?

> May 20. A letter from company president. They're interested in talking about invention. Will the broker attend a board meeting this week?

> May 23. Broker flies to the company's town. Meets with Board of Directors, answers questions about invention. Possible royalty terms are discussed. Broker conveys information that

the inventor wants a $10,000 down payment. Company president thanks broker for coming. They'll "take it up."

June 10. (Six letters and telegrams later.) Telephone call. Will the broker come over for a final conference? They're ready to do business, though there are some details to be ironed out.

June 15. Broker, accompanied by the inventor and the inventor's attorney, report to the company in morning. Negotiations concluded, and contract drawn up and signed, by the close of business.

Not until the final session was the inventor called upon to do any travelling. Even then it would not have been necessary for the inventor to be present. In most instances, in fact, it is desireable for the inventor *not* to be present. Bargaining about an invention is a tough business, and a specialized one, and generally company officials prefer to talk to the broker—even though he might strike a harder bargain than the inventor himself.

When such a negotiating conference is going on the broker asks that the inventor be reachable by telephone. If some point comes up—say a new financial offer—that requires word from him, the broker can discuss it on the phone, give the inventor time to think it over. The inventor may be able to do this better in familiar surroundings than if facing a battery of business officials.

The important thing for the inventor to remember is this: When he empowers a broker to negotiate for him, the broker does not set the terms. He makes no agreements not fully approved by the inventor. He signs no contracts on the inventor's behalf. Everything the broker does must be approved by the inventor. When a contract is worked out, it goes to the inventor for signature and approval.

This approval should always include a careful scrutiny by the inventor's personal attorney, who will, in many cases, want to make amendments in the contract.

Couldn't the attorney handle the negotiations in the first place? On occasion attorneys do, but rarely does an attorney consider himself enough of a specialist in the commercial aspects of licensing an invention to undertake the job of hammering out contract terms. Many lawyers advise their inventor clients to use the services of a broker for this phase of the selling process. Time enough, most legal experts feel, for the attorney to enter the picture when it comes time to get the exact wording of an agreement that will protect his client.

selling your invention
to the u.s. government

Can you sell your invention to the Government? You can—
but if it's essentially a non-military device, there's not much
reason to. You'll do better to sell it to private industry, which
will then sell the finished product to a government agency
which might have use for it.

Military devices, however, are a different story. The term
"military" is very elastic, as will be seen by the list at the end of
this chapter. Such inventions can be sold directly to the Government, which may purchase them on the same general terms as
would private industry.

There is no civilian agency which acts as a clearing house
for inventions offered to the Government. The inventor should
offer his invention directly to whatever branch of the Government he feels will be most likely to use it.

The following paragraphs should answer most questions you
may have about offering your invention to the Government.

● how to submit a proposal to the government

Simply mail the appropriate branch a clear, concise description of your idea or invention. Each description should contain
the following:

• 1 • A statement of each advantage which your invention possesses which makes it superior to similar devices already in use.

• 2 • Complete disclosure of the method or principle underlying the operation of your invention.

• 3 • A step-by-step description clear enough to enable an engineer to understand fully the construction and operation of your invention.

• 4 • Any drawings, diagrams or photographs necessary to describe the construction of your invention.

• 5 • Any theoretical or performance data which you have collected.

● are there any limits on the types of inventive ideas which the government will consider?

There are very few. In general, however, the government does not act on inventions of *primary* interest to a civilian industry, such as certain auto accessories, even if the inventions might someday be used by the Government. The government purchasing agencies are usually aware of these items and prefer to purchase them through regular procurement channels.

● what are some outside inventions which have been adopted by the armed services?

Soon after the attack on Pearl Harbor, a New York inventor named Samuel Ruben tackled one of the Signal Corps' most baffling problems. Batteries for "walkie-talkie" radio-telephones were losing most of their effectiveness en route to the tropics and failed in action after only two weeks. Ruben came up with a mercury dry cell battery, half the size of a standard type, yet with five times the service life. It proved so successful that, in 1944, its inventor was awarded one of ten World War II Certificates of Appreciation extended by the Signal Corps. In peace time, Ruben's remarkable battery has made possible the miniaturization of hearing aids, portable transistor radios, and many other devices.

On an other occasion, a young radio mechanic invented a portable mine detector which could spot metals buried up to 30 inches in the ground. The best British and German detectors were useless on mines buried deeper than six inches. The detector was adopted in time to save thousands of Allied lives during World War II.

Other inventions used by the services include the electrical firing device for the bazooka, an antirust coating, and an anti-aircraft sight.

• does an invention have to be patented before it is submitted to the government?

It does not. A large percentage of the inventions submitted are not patented, and many useful ideas could not be patented even if the originator wished them to be.

• does the government accept models?

No. It asks that an inventor does not accompany his description and disclosure form with any sort of model. If examination of a written description indicates that a model would be helpful in evaluating an invention, the inventor will be notified.

• does the government accept chemical samples?

Unsolicited chemical samples will be promptly destroyed without examination, as they might prove dangerous to staff members. Chemical proposals should include formulae, methods of preparation, laboratory data, and other information to permit evaluation by qualified chemists.

● can an inventor discuss his invention with an official of the government in Washington?

Yes, but you should realize before you spend time and money going to Washington that your visit isn't likely to produce immediate results. Since the arsenals, laboratories, and proving grounds where tests are conducted are now widely scattered over the United States, a trip to Washington does not usually hasten the review process. Once an agency shows interest in a written proposal, it will make arrangements for any personal consultation at the appropriate technical facility. In short, your idea will get just as prompt and thorough attention if it is submitted by mail.

● how long does it take to hear from the government?

Whatever the decision on your invention, you will be notified as soon as possible. At all times, correspondence is handled in the order in which it is received. It is futile, in other words, to write for information about an earlier proposal. The original proposal will be studied and processed before your second letter. If you wish immediate acknowledgment of a proposal, you may send it by certified mail, return receipt requested.

If your invention is referred to other agencies, you will be so informed. If the technical group to which it is referred wants further information, it will get in touch with you.

● **if an inventor is reluctant to file a patent application on his invention because he believes the publication of the granted patent would be detrimental to the national defense, is there a special method of handling his case?**

You need have no qualms about filing an application in the U.S. Patent Office. If it is determined that publication of the invention by the granting of a patent would be detrimental to the national defense, the Commissioner of Patents will order that the invention be kept secret and will withhold the grant of a patent until such time as a decision is made that disclosure of the invention is no longer deemed detrimental to the national security.

● **if an invention is not patented, how does the government protect an inventor's rights?**

The Government has many of its personnel and contractors constantly working on research and development for improving all types of material and the substance of a proposal may already be known to Government employees or Government contractors, or already be in the public domain.

Accordingly, it has been found to be desirable, in receiving proposals for evaluation, to exercise such precaution as will preclude misunderstanding by the submitter of the proposal and will prevent the receipt of such proposals from having any restrictive or limiting effect on Government research and development.

In view of these considerations, it is believed that as a condition to receiving and evaluating your proposal it should be understood that the acceptance does not imply a promise to pay, a recognition of novelty or originality or a contractual relationship such as would render the Government liable to pay for any use of the information to which it would otherwise fully be entitled.

However, the Government has no intention of using any proposal, in which you have property rights, without proper compensation, and will, in the evaluation process, restrict your information to those persons having an official need for the information for purposes of evaluation.

One precautionary measure taken by the Government is to date-stamp all incoming mail. While no actual protection accrues from this practice, since a proposal becomes a part of permanent Government records, it is always available as evidence in any subsequent controversy over priority of inventorship.

● does the government ever agree to purchase an invention before it has been fully disclosed?

Even the most sincerely offered "pig-in-a-poke" cannot be adequately appraised without inspection. The Government is both unwilling and unable to agree to any conditions concerning adoption or payment before an invention is disclosed. Policy in this matter is the same as that in private industry (see Chapter 11).

● does the government need the kind of inventions which can be developed by independent inventors?

A study of various inventions desired by various branches of the Government reveals that most are of a nature best tackled by a research organization. However, some are within the scope of the independent inventor.

The following descriptions of inventions wanted, as stated in government bulletins, is presented only as a sampling of requirements. Of course, you should realize that, at the time you read this book, these particular needs may no longer be unfulfilled.

Static discharge system. A lightweight, positive action system to eliminate static electricity from helicopters for loading and unloading operations. These static electric charges build up in the helicopters during flight. Eliminating this static will make the handling of sensitive explosives safer for the cargo and personnel involved.

Fastening means. A piece to function as a bolt or cap screw that can be operated without the usual amount of turning. If such a device can be developed, the underlying principle might also be applied to a new design for a gun breech that would replace a sliding or rotating breech block. In both designs, multiplicity of parts is undesirable.

Self-cleaning oil filters. Self-cleaning, lubricating oil filters energized by the oil pressure system. Should be capable of filtering out sludge and dirt particles as small as 20 microns. The military is trying to reduce the time expended in maintenance of oil filters, yet protect components such as engines and transmissions.

Traction aid for wheeled vehicles. A traction aid for wheeled vehicles which can be easily applied to either the wheel or tire.

Techniques for incorporating additives to soils. New concepts for mixing a soil stabilizer into wet sticky soils are needed. Present techniques require either extremely cumbersome machinery or are inefficient or both. Concept must be capable of being utilized by lightweight, highly mobile equipment and must be able to achieve an intimate blend of soil with either a dry powder or a liquid. It is desirable to be able to accomplish stabilizer incorporation rapidly to depths as great as two feet with a minimum of manipulation of the soil.

A dry battery heater. A battery heater with following characteristics: (1) use fuels commonly found in the military supply systems, such as gasoline or kerosene, (2) start at temperatures as low as —40° F, (3) controllable at all ambient conditions likely to be encountered by infantry soldiers, (4) high ratio of space and weight to heat energy generated, (5) easily and simply refueled under field conditions, (6) rugged construction, (7) adaptable to a variety of form-factors to match battery sizes, shapes, and heating requirements, (8) operable for long periods with a requirement for refueling only, (9) usable in confined space, (10) can be built into dry batteries composed of an assembly of cells, (11) cost per unit even with small or moderate production not higher than the cost of three of the batteries it will heat.

Relative humidity sensor. An instrument is needed for the measurement of relative humidity over the range 4 to 100% with an accuracy of 2.0% over the entire range. The sensor should possess the following characteristics: (1) long term stability, (2) rapid response—2 to 4 seconds, (3) light weight; readily portable, (4) sufficiently rugged design to withstand extreme conditions of blowing dust and sand, (5) should not require water or plumbing of any sort, (6) should not require filters which must be changed after every dust storm.

Instrumentation to study the reactions of active human test subjects when subjected to environmental stress. Skin thermocouples and rectal thermometers have been developed which can be worn by active clothed test subjects. These sensors, together with their associated instrumentation are reliable, convenient and do not cause discomfort to the subject. More recently, a telemetering system for measuring pulse rates consisting of a sensor and a small transistorized radio transmitter has been designed which can continuously measure heart beats and is now ready for user tests. Similiar telemetering devices are required for measuring cardiac output, oxygen consumption, tidal volume, breathing rate and chemical components of the breath.

Simple shock recorder. A need exists for a simple economical device that will measure the magnitude of shock applied in any direction. Time of the shock would also be highly desirable. This device would be incorporated in packages during shipment to determine maximum loads encountered in the transportation environment. Currently available devices of this nature are unsatisfactory since they measure in a single plane and do not reliably measure the vector sum of the applied shock. A design for such a unit should encompass the following parameters: (1) compact, (2) lightweight, (3) expendable, if possible, from an economic standpoint, (4) not a "go" or "no go" device, (5) capable of measuring acceleration in any plane, (6) capable of measuring time of shock.

should you start your own business?

Should an inventor start his own business to manufacture and sell his invention? It's a momentous question and a difficult one to answer.

On the one hand there is the fact that some of the greatest successes in the field of independent invention have been achieved by those who chose to make their own. Perhaps the most impressive success of all, that of Edwin Land, would never have been so spectacular had the young inventor of Polaroid sold his discovery to another company. There's not much question that the fortune he holds today would be considerably smaller than the $100,000,000 it is had he not started his own enterprise.

On the other hand there is the dismal fact that probably the majority of inventors who start their own companies meet with business failure. A newly formed small company, producing a new product based on an invention, has some formidable problems not encountered by new concerns setting out to make and market established, standard products.

The best advice we can give any inventor toying with the idea of starting his own company is to recognize the fact that the odds are against him. Only under certain special conditions should you take the plunge—and then only if you really want to be a businessman and have the capacities to be one, or can bring into your company personnel competent to run the business end of things. And, of course, you must have the necessary capital—or be able to acquire it. (See Chapter 15.)

We can't in this small space tell how or how not to set up and run a new, small business. *How to Make Money in Your Own Business,* by Ernest Field (Prentice-Hall, 1965) can give you some advice on the subject. (Also see the *Reference Guide* for list of additional helpful books.)

● can you lick the production problem?

No matter how many good reasons he has for starting his own business, or how many factors such a business has in its favor, no one can make a go of it if he hasn't solved the problem of economical, trouble-free production. It is a must that any small business have a product that is readily turned out, and this is doubly a requisite for the inventor who, whatever his capabilities, is not usually qualified, professionally or financially, to deal with difficult production problems. Failure at this point has wrecked many an inventor's hopes.

Fortunately there is a short-cut to production that does not involve buying your own machinery, with all the attendant costs and headaches. You can turn to contract production. Let a firm that is already in the business of manufacturing take on the job for you.

A good example of its advantages is shown in the case of Ove Hanson of Seattle. Hanson invented the *Squangle,* a versatile handyman's and carpenter's tool that accurately squares material and measures level and plumb.

Hanson found his *Squangle* could be produced on standard stamping machines which he could purchase and install in a plant of his own. However, he also found several local machine shops which had these same machines. Without setting up a factory of his own, he could have the parts stamped out for him by any of these firms with no machinery investment at all on his part. He was able to get low cost quotations by placing standing orders with several firms, so that they ran them off in down time when their machines would otherwise have been idle.

Hanson's unit costs over a period of years might have run a little lower had he owned his own machines, but this hypothetical long-run advantage was more than offset by the no-risk, no-investment benefits of the contract production.

If you don't find a concern in your own community that can handle production of your item, consult the advertisements in trade journals and in the "Manufacturing Facilities" columns of major newspapers, such as the New York *Times*. Typical advertisements read:

> "Metal Stamping of All Kinds. Open Time. In modern well equipped plant, running 24 hours a day. Ample storage facilities." Or "Injection moldings of all types. Open time available on speed presses."

Some firms go farther than production. They will assemble, package and store your product for you. However, many inventors who have started their own companies prefer to do this work themselves. Ove Hanson chose to assemble and pack the stamped parts for his *Squangle* in his home garage.

Foreign production is a possibility of which some inventors have availed themselves. One successful inventor of novelty items has them produced in Japan. On an item designed to retail at $9.95, he got production estimates in the U.S. of $3.00, too high to provide the necessary spread between manufacturer's cost and retail price. (See Chapter 6.) He was able to have the same item turned out expertly by a Japanese firm for $1.50.

• can you lick the sales problem?

How are you going to sell it? This is often a tougher question to answer than the one about how you're going to produce it. But you must have an answer, and a good one, before you ever go into the business of making your invention.

We've seen far too many situations in which the inventor of a basically saleable item went ahead and started production without really solving the sales problem. We know one inventor who did everything right up to this point. He had a first rate invention to start with, he got his patent, and he checked market possibilities. His production costs were within reason.

His product, a novelty item, was ideally suited for sale in hardware stores. The trouble was that he hadn't really set up a method of selling it to them. The circulars he had printed and mailed out, along with order blanks, to 5,000 hardware stores, brought back fewer than a hundred orders for a trial dozen. The business folded, with a total loss of the $10,000 the inventor had put into his venture.

The tragedy is that the failure was needless. The inventor thought the merits of his gadget were so obvious and so impressive that all he had to do was point them out in the circulars sent to hardware stores. These merchants, he felt, would instantly see the profit possibilities in handling his wares. He reckoned without the fact that this is simply not the way merchants are induced to take on a line of merchandise. They've got to be sold. And it takes salesmen to do that.

Actually, there is a way by which this inventor could have acquired a sales force, at very little cost to himself. Many successful inventor-founded companies are using it. Ove Hanson, a craftsman himself, thoroughly checked the market for *Squangle*. He knew that it was big and that the tool had to be sold through hardware stores and lumberyards. He also knew what the unfortunate inventor described above didn't know: He had to have salesmen. On the other hand, he was sure he couldn't afford to set up a sales staff simply to sell this one tool.

His solution was to turn to an existent sales force. In the U.S. there are several thousand "manufacturer's representatives," sales organizations, or individuals who carry a line of a number of different non-competitive kinds of merchandise. These firms and individuals advertise their services in the classified columns of newspapers, in trade journals, and in the telephone book's Yellow Pages. Many actively seek promising new items, and particularly welcome those that have never before been offered.

Customarily, the products they handle are sold on a commission basis, so an inventor-manufacturer engaging such sales representation has no payroll. The representatives are in no sense employees, but are, instead, contractors.

A typical advertisement for such a firm reads:

"Sales Agency—Florida. Calling on drug chains, drug wholesalers, department stores, rack jobbers. Aggressive sales ability. Wants sundry, specialty, cosmetic and drug lines."

Another reads:

"Recognized manufacturer's representative. Calling on hardware trade, New Jersey, Pennsylvania, New York City. Proven sales record. Seeks novelty items."

An inventor can contact the people who place these advertisements, or he can run his own. However he does it, he should do as Ove Hanson did, and get his sales set up taken care of before going into any kind of major production.

To deal successfully with potential representatives you'll need circulars that describe your invention, samples of the actual product, and some sort of evidence of sales potential. You have to convince the representatives of two things: (1)

that you've got a winner that will make money for them. (You'll be able to put to good use any "marketability search" you've carried out.) and, (2) that you are responsible, a reliable source of the item you're offering. They don't want to go out and get orders and then find themselves unable to deliver.

There is one other short cut to acquiring a sales force. Many firms which sell products by mail, issuing elaborate catalogs and running advertisements in magazines, are on the lookout for new items.

The existence of these firms helped Don Poynter, of Cincinnati, an inventor of novelties that might be called "toys for adults." Most famous of them is the fabulous *Little Black Box.* If you press a button on it, the cover slowly rises, and from the box emerges a plastic hand, which also pushes the button, and then withdraws back into the box as the cover comes down. This seemingly pointless little gadget has proved to be very much to the point for Poynter, who has seen its sales mount past a half million units. A wide segment of the population, including sophisticated scientists and professors, admit their fascination with this spoof of the mechanical age.

Poynter found it necessary to spend very little money for sales expense. He simply turned to jobbers who sold items by mail. Since he was an advertising copy writer by profession, he had no difficulty preparing the circulars which brought in orders from these firms. It was not necessary to use personal salesmanship to induce them to handle his product, since they are accustomed to considering items offered them by mail. Of course, he had a number of things going for him that are necessary to anyone with an invention designed for this market—flashy sales appeal, extreme novelty, long profit for the selling companies. The last is extremely important.

The list of inventions successfully sold through direct mail firms is growing, and it appears to be one of the most promising sales outlets for gadget-type items. A chemical hand-warmer, a pocket alarm to remind a driver his parking meter time is running out, a dog feeding tray, a reel-type key chain—these are just a few of the patented items that have been sold in this manner.

If you think your invention might qualify for this market, you'd do well to study some of the advertisements in the mail-order sections of big newspapers and magazines. Can your invention sell in the price range of comparable items? Do the things you can say about it have the kind of appeal these advertisements have?

This is a fast-changing field, with new concerns entering it constantly. You should consult recent advertisements in the above-mentioned media for names and addresses of such firms.

● want to keep it a secret?

A few inventors have, for special reasons, decided not to patent their inventions, but to keep them secret. These inventors have had to either set up their own companies or deal with companies in which they already had an interest. It's pretty hard to sell a "secret" invention to another company.

There's no law that says you have to get a patent, and if your invention is a chemical formula or a production machine it is possible that secrecy, rather than patenting, will be better protection.

The most profitable of major secret inventions was Richard Harris' *Toni* home permanent. It is doubtful if Harris could have interested any existent concern in his invention. And, of course, if he had patented it, finding similar formulae would have been relatively easy for the chemists of other firms, as indeed proved to be the case afterwards. However Harris got a good head-start, and was able to sell his pioneering company for $20,-000,000.

Another secret invention success story was that of Carl Kastner, who developed a chemical mixture for curing concrete. In royalties paid him by a company in which he had an interest, Kastner received an average return of $11,927 per year for a period reported in a court case.

Other similarly recorded cases include that of Franklin Speicher of Pittsburgh, who invented a machine for making steel stamps. From a firm set up by backers, he derived a royalty of five per cent on steel stamps sold. Only five machines were ever made, but they turned out enough stamps to bring Speicher approximately $100,000 in royalties and salary (he was employed by the company as part of his return) in a three-year period.

So it is apparent that there are certain special cases in which secrecy is a sound policy. However, the circumstances warranting it are so unusual that we don't think it's a promising possibility for many inventors. It is unlikely to attract investors as readily as a good solid patent.

● lessons in success

There are many stories of independent inventors, who started their own enterprises, but they follow no one pattern which can serve as an infallible guide to other inventors. Each invention is so different, and the capabilities, outlook, and situation of each inventor so different that it is impossible to generalize.

However, every account of men who have been successful making their own inventions provides hints that can prove valuable to other inventors. We'd like to give you some of these stories and let you draw your own conclusions. Do any of them come close to your situation? If they do, perhaps they can become a factor in helping you decide this important question: **Should you start your own business?**

● Joseph Sunnen's garage inventions

Joseph Sunnen had a lot of ideas for inventions that would be useful around automobile service garages. The first he actually patented was an improved type of valve lifter which could be installed by mechanics to replace the original valve lifters.

Early in the day he decided that there wasn't much chance of selling his invention to an existent company. And, anyway, Sunnen had ideas about the future. He had visions of making a whole line of Sunnen products, of which the valve lifters were just a start. Sunnen took to the road to sell them, got orders, came back to the lathe in his garage to make them. When sales grew he hired others to take over both production and selling. More inventions were added to his line—a machine for fitting piston wrist pins with connecting rods, a rod aligner, a portable crankshaft grinder. All useful tools, they are sold nationally to garages, to the tune, today, of $7,000,000 a year.

This inventor had many factors in his favor when he embarked on his own business. He knew his field; he could act as his own salesman and his own producer; and he had, right from the start, a clear knowledge that he would have other inventions which could make up a "line." With a single invention he couldn't have built the big enterprise he has today. His variety of inventions makes for lower costs of sales, production and overhead.

A number of other inventors—particularly in the field of industrial or shop equipment—have followed the same path to success. But it takes a pretty special combination of abilities, as exemplified in Joseph Sunnen, to build this kind of invention-based business.

● Carl Weller's soldering gun

Carl Weller invented a new type of soldering gun, which he was able to patent. However, he could find no buyers among established companies, though he offered it to dozens of them.

After six years of vain efforts to sell it, Weller realized that if he was going to do anything with his invention, he'd have to do it fast. His patent had run through a third of its life already. At this point he went down to his basement lab, made up 274 guns by hand, and set out to sell them himself. They sold, and at a profit, even though his price, allowing for a fair return on his labor, was much higher than it would have to be in quantity production.

On the strength of this convincing sale, Weller was able to get backing and go into full scale manufacturing. Today his Weller Electric Corp., which also makes some other Weller inventions, has three factories—one in Pennsylvania and two in Puerto Rico.

Weller is one of the rare individuals who succeeded in the risky game of starting a business after existent firms have turned an invention down.

Now the other companies *can* be wrong, as Weller and a number of other inventors have proved. However, any inventor who ends up with a turned down invention should think a long time about taking a jump which others, already set up for it, refused to take. The advisability of starting your own business under these circumstances should be determined through analysis of the reasons for the rejection by other concerns.

Let us assume to start with that a thorough canvass of all likely prospects has been made by a reputable broker or by you. First, check to see if there is a consistent pattern to the rejections, insofar as you know the reasons for them. (Unfortunately, not all of the concerns receiving inventions reveal their reasons for turning them down.)

If the companies which did state their objections gave reasons such as "it won't sell" . . . "insufficient market" . . . "not enough demand" . . . "sales expense too high to warrant manufacture" . . . you should certainly beware of trying to do it yourself. Unless, by some kind of market survey, you have established good evidence that there is a market, and that you know just how to reach it.

Whatever you have done up to this point, you probably should undertake further studies on your own to find out if the companies which turned it down really are right. Some of the ways you can do this are outlined in Chapter 6. Ideally, you will conduct a small scale test sale, even if that involves having samples made up at a small quantity price far above that of larger production runs.

If your invention was rejected because of production problems, you'll have to determine on your own whether these objections apply only to the companies which considered your invention or are basic to the invention itself.

You just may be able to beat the game. The inventor of a novelty item was turned down by 40 companies on the grounds that the plastic tubing his gadget used could not be bent by their equipment. Not taking no for an answer, the inventor hunted around among contract shops, finally found one that had a machine that could bend the tubing. It offered to do this part of production for 12½ ¢ a unit, compared to the prohibitive 88¢ to $1 that various prospective manufacturers had averred it would cost.

● Stanley Mendell's desk top computer

In the basement of his home, Stanley Mendell, to whom mathematics is a hobby, devised a desk top analog computer.

While this sounds formidable, actually his device is quite the opposite. What he developed is essentially an aluminum board on which gauges representing mathematical quantities are moved in horizontal slots.

Mendell's computer was the only desk-top contrivance that could do what big electronic digital computers could, and his market survey told him that nobody else had hit on a small device that could be used right on the job for hundreds of tasks it wouldn't pay to turn over to a big computer. Moreover, Mendell found that there was a real need for such a device, and that industry would willingly pay a price that would make it very profitable to produce. These conclusions were borne out when he set up his own company and orders poured in for the *Planalogs,* selling at about $400 each.

Mendell succeeded because he had a really needed item, exclusive in its field. Not many inventions meet this specification, but when they do, the odds are upped for the inventor-manufacturer.

● Ross Williams' wash 'n dri

When Ross Williams, who invented lotion-saturated towels for waterless washing (see Chapter 6), developed them in his kitchen laboratory, he soon realized he had a real marketing problem. Big toiletries companies, sounded out, were less than enthusiastic. Yet certainly he had a product which could best be handled by a big company.

Williams was in the fortunate position of being able to raise the capital for such a company. *Wash 'n Dri* enjoyed sales of $1,000,000 the first year. In the marketplace it proved itself so attractive that the company was acquired, on terms favorable to Ross and the stockholders, by Palmolive-Peet.

Other inventors have found themselves in Williams' position, with an invention on their hands that just doesn't interest industry *as an invention*, but which has great appeal once it is the product of a going concern.

Starting a business and then selling out is an opportunity not open to many inventors but for some it offers a chance for the biggest profits.

● Arthur Johnson's target thrower

One autumn when he was hunting wild turkey in Pennsylvania, Arthur M. Johnson, a retired Naval officer, stopped to do a little target practice. Both he and the friend who was with him strained their arms tossing aloft the empty beer cans they used for targets.

"There must be an easier way to do this," Johnson opined, as his muscles began to ache. He went home and fashioned his *Targeteer*, a gun that throws a beer can by the propulsive force of a blank cartridge.

Johnson knew he had a good invention because he is an expert marksman himself and has many sportsmen friends. In fact, his first move after he had made up his first two *Targeteers* was to lend them to friends, one of whom was Pete Brown, the gun editor of *Sports Afield*. Brown tried the device out on his Arizona ranch, approved it, wrote an article about it in his magazine. It was also publicized and recommended in John Stuart Martin's authoritative book, *Learning to Gun*.

On the strength of his standing in the field, and this send-off for his invention, Johnson could readily have found a company that would purchase rights to making it. Instead, he decided that, with sales channels open and the production problems simple, he could make far more money by manufacturing it himself, selling by mail and in major sporting goods stores. His judgment was confirmed by first year sales of 20,000 units, largely mail orders.

Going into business for himself made good sense in Johnson's case because he knew thoroughly the market into which he was venturing. He already had a fine head start for his product because of all the favorable publicity it had received before manufacture.

• George Nelson's stud welder

George Nelson was a mechanic at the time he invented the *Nelson Stud Welder* gun which welds a flux-filled stud to metal, eliminating drilling and tapping operations. Used in shipbuilding and other metal work, it promised huge savings in labor and time. The advantages of the device were so obvious that Nelson, who could have sold it to another company, decided that he would be better off having a share in the stock of his own company—even a small share. Actually, to raise the capital, he found it necessary to sell 80% of the stock.

Within three years his gun had so proved its possibilities that a larger corporation came forward with an irresistible offer —$15,000,000. Nelson walked off with a cool $3,000,000, in addition to the salary and other benefits he had received during the time his company operated.

It should be noted that Nelson's invention was perfect for this kind of return—it was a "big" invention, greatly superior to anything in existence. It could quickly demonstrate its superiority. It could be made by a small company because production problems were not great. Sales problems were negligible because Nelson worked in the field in which it would have to be sold and knew just what kind of salesmen to hire.

He was a "know-the-ropes" inventor who ran less risk in playing for big stakes than many an inventor who doesn't know his field would be running in playing for much smaller stakes.

15

financial backing for your invention

"How do I get backing for my invention?"

As long as there have been inventions this has been the plaintive question of the inventor who needs financial help at the developmental stage of his invention.

There is no national organization that "sponsors" the independent inventor. Anyway, the inventor of a worthwhile device stands a better chance of getting help right in his own community.

As Joseph Berman, noted patent expert, puts it in the *Journal of the Patent Office Society*: "Backers of some inventors have often shared in their good fortune. [Today] the tax law gives them clear advantages. It therefore does not consume too big a share of an investor's income to become an angel for an inventor whose work has possibilities."

The tax break is this: If the invention pays out, the backer's return can be treated as capital gains, with its lower tax rate. On the other hand, if the invention fails, he can deduct the entire loss from ordinary income. These are generalizations, subject to modifications due to special circumstances, but this is the basic reason why the tax laws make it easier to find investors in the admittedly speculative enterprise of developing a new invention.

• local backers are easiest to find

The tax situation, coupled with the fact that there are more people today in the higher tax brackets, makes it more likely that the inventor will find a backer among friends and acquaintances. In a survey conducted by the authors of *The Successful Inventor's Guide,* it was found that doctors, dentists, lawyers and engineers, as well as businessmen, had invested money in the development of inventions by local inventors.

The mid-western inventor of a golfing device readily found three backers among fellow members of his country club. An engineer who invented a toy received an offer of investment from his attorney. (Not his patent attorney, but his regular local attorney, who handled his other legal affairs.) A high school teacher who devised a photographic device got backing from an M.D. who was a member of the school board.

It is almost impossible to give an inventor sound advice about just what kind of an arrangement he should make with a person who backs him in developing his invention. The situation varies too much from one invention to another to permit making general rules. We've known of cases in which the inventor had to take in several backers, and ended up with a very small interest in his own invention.

There is one sound rule, however, that any inventor should follow: Don't seek financial help too early in the game. A few extra months of getting the bugs out of your invention, a little extra time and money spent finding out about its market possibilities on your own, may change the whole picture of how much money you need, and the terms on which you get it. This is particularly true of the "marketability search" we so strongly recommend making. Nothing is more impressive to potential investors than concrete evidence that you really have a product that has real sales possibilities.

If your need for the money is to develop your invention to the point where you can have samples made for more extensive consumer checking, you can at least carry out the preliminary checks that don't require models. (See Chapter 6.) If your market checking comes out negatively, this go-slow signal may save you from seeking an investment in a losing venture.

When you seek a backer at the developmental stage of your invention, you should be aware of certain legal facts particularly pertinent to the inventor's situation.

For instance, if you should sell your backer a part share in your patent, you lose all control over what he does with your invention. Don't think that if you sell him 49 percent of your patent and retain 51 percent you've got a veto power over him. You do not, because the law is that a man who owns a share in a patent, however small it is, can sell it or license it to whomever he wishes, on whatever terms he likes. The other part-owner or owners have nothing to say about it—except that they get their share of whatever money such an agreement brings in. Of course, he or they cannot stop you from doing what you want either. Certain agreements made without benefit of legal counsel have caused a lot of trouble for unwary inventors.

What you do, therefore, is to sell, not a share in your patent, but a share in the proceeds from it, so that you retain control of the patent.

Another legal consideration is a situation in which your backer wishes to be listed as co-inventor of the invention into which he puts money for development. He cannot be called a co-inventor unless he has personally contributed ideas to the technical development. If you run into trouble later, your whole patent can be invalidated on the basis of false information given in the application.

These examples of legal fine points provide ample reason for having a good, knowledgeable lawyer on your side, as doubt-less any prospective backer will have on his. That way you can't get cheated, nor can you enter into some agreement that will turn out to have unfortunate consequences. Even if you are making the agreement with your best friend, or a close relative, for both your protection and his, you should let an attorney guide you in all legal arrangements.

• find a company to take over

Some inventors, though not many, have found a way, other than cash investment by a backer, to get assistance in developing their inventions. Though not widely available, it consists of finding a company which will, on some basis, purchase your invention, and also take over the development problems. The oil burner firm which acquired rights in a patented, but not commercially developed, oil feeding device from the inventor, was willing to take on the burden, because it was thus enabled to adapt the improved device directly to its particular product.

The same was true of a rubber maker which took over a partly developed machine which needed a great amount of work before it was truly operative. It fitted so well into the pattern of the company's production that it seemed a desirable investment.

In both these cases the inventor had a fairly technical development of the kind which might well have emerged from the research and development department of a company in the field.

An inventor who had particular success with using purchasing-company backing, Carl G. Dreymann of Pittsburgh, made an arrangement which might be open to other technically competent inventors. A paper box manufacturer which Dreymann gave an exclusive license, agreed to pay him a nominal salary of $200 a month while he was working on the development of his invention, a waterproofing compound. Dreymann also got five percent of gross sales. The arrangement worked out well, and in the nine years after the patent was granted,

Dreymann and his daughter, who worked with him, received over $175,000 in royalties.

Companies manufacturing consumer products are understandably more reluctant about taking over development problems. However, when an invention seems to promise returns that warrant the expenditure, an exception is sometimes made to the rule that the only outside inventions purchased are those that are ready to go without putting a burden on company facilities. One striking example was Major Jack Dixon's *Pitch Back*, the baseball-returning device. Engineers of the purchasing company spent hundreds of hours and thousands of dollars in readying the invention for full commercial production.

• capital for your own company

The inventor who has decided to set up his own company to make and sell his invention will also find his sources of capital close to home. And in general, if he really has an invention advanced enough and promising enough to warrant setting out to manufacture it, he'll find it relatively easier to raise money than the inventor seeking development capital. It goes almost without saying that the company should be set up as a corporation, with certain shares retained by the inventor, certain others sold to provide the needed capital.

While we can't go into all the ins and outs of setting up a corporation, these case histories of the way it was done by three typical success-minded inventors should be instructive.

Louis Korter, a Seattle jeweler, got to thinking about aluminum siding and asked himself why this light, versatile metal wouldn't also make good shingles? He repaired to his basement workshop, applied some knowledge he had acquired years before when he'd been a sheet metal worker, and, after considerable experimentation, came up with what he'd visualized—an aluminum shingle that locked ingeniously with the ones next to it. He applied for a patent and eventually got one. For all the research done in the light metals field, aluminum shingles had not been developed by any of the big aluminum companies.

His production know-how, and preliminary checks he made concerning the market for his shingles, convinced Korter that he could profitably manufacture them himself. His problem was the familiar one: He had little money to invest. He turned to a neighbor, Victor Nielson, who invested $22,000 in the corporation, Aluminum Lock Shingle Company, which Korter set up.

For his patent, Korter received 102 of the 200 shares issued. Nielson received 44 shares. Twenty more shares were sold to other investors, for a total of $10,000. At a later date, Korter bought back the stock. By the fifth year in business, the company, as reported in *Fortune*, was grossing $3,000,000.

A woman inventor, Mrs. Bertha E. Thomas, must be rated among the most successful practitioners of the inventor-owned-company path to getting the most out of an invention. In her case, it involved more than one invention. Her innovations were in the technical field of flexible couplings, on which she was granted four different patents.

Setting up the Thomas Flexible Coupling Company, she assigned two patents to the concern in exchange for 450 shares of stock. She also signed an agreement with her own company to pay her a ten percent royalty on the gross sale price. On the two patents she did not assign the company she received an outright payment from the company of $3,500, plus a contract for royalties. However, she kept the right to license them in certain non-competitive fields.

It appeared that Mrs. Thomas had made too good a deal with Thomas Flexible Coupling, and she later granted the concern an exclusive license. Her royalties reached a comfortable figure. For the five years in which they were made public as the result of a court case, she received the following: First year, $170,-833.10; second year, $240,323.73; third year, $80,000; fourth year, $17,978.35; fifth year, $33,089.41.

Since she also owned a considerable block of stock in a prospering company based on her invention, it can certainly be said that Mrs. Thomas' method of financing her invention was well chosen.

Ross Williams, whose success we described earlier, knew that he would need a great deal of capital to go into the manufacture of his invention, the lotion-impregnated tissues for waterless washing. The sums that could be obtained from friends and acquaintances would not be enough.

His method was to organize a company in Canaan, Connecticut. The Canaan Industrial Development Association, Inc., as it was called, promised to bring a worthwhile industry to the community. Shares sold to 125 local citizens brought in the needed $250,000 to start operations. Williams drew a salary and received a royalty for his invention. Reported sales volume the first year of operation was $1,000,000.

● help in financing your invention-based company

The Small Business Administration is an agency which can help give your small, invention-based business a financial boost. Sale of stock may not be sufficient to provide such a company with all the capital needed, and it's sometimes not too easy for a new concern to qualify for bank loans (although bankers take a much kindlier view toward such enterprises than they once did). This is exactly where the SBA comes into the picture.

Early in 1964, the Small Business Investment Act became law. Its aim is to encourage a larger flow of private capital to small companies. The law permits some 700 federally-licensed but privately-owned investment firms to invest larger amounts than formerly in small companies which qualify for such help.

You can get all details from your nearest Small Business Administration office (see list in the *Reference Guide*). There you can also get valuable counsel on various aspects of setting up a small company.

In all phases of getting your company going you should not neglect what can prove to be the decisive source of help in your enterprise. Go to the local Chamber of Commerce. You will find the secretary interested in anything that might bring a new business to the community. While the C of C isn't going to lend you money, or even recommend you to a banker, the secretary does know the businessmen in his organization and may well put you in touch with potential investors. Certainly he'll go to great lengths to help you get production facilities, personnel, and publicity.

After all, working with you may help develop a local business like hundreds of invention-based concerns scattered across the country. Perhaps a giant like Polaroid Corporation, which, it should be remembered, was founded by independent inventor Edwin Land, maybe a modest concern employing only a dozen or so people—but certainly valuable to your town or city whatever its size.

What community would not welcome the $7,000,000 a year Sunnen Products Company of St. Louis, which makes the ingenious garage equipment invented by Joseph Sunnen? Or the Easton, Pennsylvania plant where George Weller annually makes some $5,000,000 worth of soldering guns, power sanders, and other Weller inventions? Or the Cherokee, Iowa factory in which 200 employees turn out the machines dreamed up by Vernon Lundell, including the truck hoist which first made him exclaim, even as you may have done, "I've got a million-dollar invention!"

appendix

the inventor's reference guide

- ● **answers to questions frequently asked of the patent office**

While many of the questions below have been answered at some length in this book, these succinct replies made by the Patent Office will serve as a review of major points and clarify certain details of concern to inventors.

Meaning of Words "Patent Pending"

1. *Q. What do the terms "patent pending" and "patent applied for" mean?*

A. They are used by a manufacturer or seller of an article to inform the public that an application for patent on that article is on file in the Patent Office. The law imposes a fine on those who use these terms falsely to deceive the public.

Patent Applications

2. *Q. I have made some changes and improvements in my invention after my patent application was filed in the Patent Office. May I amend my patent application by adding a description or illustration of these features?*

A. No. The law specifically provides that new matter shall not be introduced into the disclosure of a patent application. However, you should call the attention of your attorney or agent promptly to any such changes you may make or plan to make, so that he may take or recommend any steps that may be necessary for your protection.

3. *Q. How does one apply for a patent?*

A. By making the proper application to the Commissioner of Patents, Washington D.C. 20025.

4. *Q. Of what does a patent application consist?*

A. An application fee, a petition, a specification and claims describing and defining the invention, an oath, and a drawing if the invention can be illustrated.

5. *Q. What are the Patent Office fees in connection with filing of an application for patent and issuance of the patent?*

A. A filing fee of $30 plus $1 for each claim in excess of 20 is required when the application is filed. A final fee of $30 plus $1 for each claim allowed in excess of 20 is also required if the patent is to be granted. This final fee is not required until your application is allowed by the Patent Office.

6. *Q. Are models required as part of the application?*

A. Only in the most exceptional cases. The Patent Office has the power to require that a model be furnished, but rarely exercises it.

7. *Q. Is it necessary to go to the Patent Office in Washington to transact business concerning patent matters?*

A. No; most business with the Patent Office is conducted by correspondence. Interviews regarding pending applications can be arranged with examiners if necessary, however, and are often helpful.

8. *Q. Can the Patent Office give advice as to whether an inventor should apply for a patent?*

A. No. It can only consider the patentability of an invention when this question comes regularly before it in the form of a patent application.

9. *Q. Is there any danger that the Patent Office will give others information contained in my application while it is pending?*

A. No. All patent applications are maintained in the strictest secrecy until the patent is issued. After the patent is issued, however, the Patent Office file containing the application and all correspondence leading up to issuance of the patent is made available in the Patent Office Search Room for inspection by anyone, and copies of these files may be purchased from the Patent Office.

10. *Q. May I write to the Patent Office directly about my application after it is filed?*

A. The Patent Office will answer an applicant's inquiries as to the status of the application, and inform him whether his application has been rejected, allowed, or is awaiting action by the Patent Office. However, if you have a patent attorney or agent the Patent Office cannot correspond with both you and the attorney concerning the merits of your application. All comments concerning your invention should be forwarded through your patent attorney or agent.

11. *Q. What happens when two inventors apply separately for a patent for the same invention?*

A. An "interference" is declared and testimony may be submitted to the Patent Office to determine which inventor is entitled to the patent. Your attorney or agent can give you further information about this if it becomes necessary.

12. *Q. Can the six-month period allowed by the Patent Office for response to an official action in a pending application be extended?*

A. No. This time is fixed by law and cannot be extended by the Patent Office. The application will become abandoned unless proper response is received in the Patent Office within this time limit.

When To Apply for Patent

13. *Q. I have been making and selling my invention for the past 13 months and have not filed any patent application. Is is too late for me to apply for patent?*

A. Yes. A valid patent may not be obtained if the invention was in public use or on sale in this country for more than one year prior to the filing of your patent application. Your own use and sale of the invention for more than a year before your application is filed will bar your right to a patent just as effectively as though this use and sale had been made by someone else.

14. *Q. I published an article describing my invention in a magazine 13 months ago. Is it too late to apply for patent?*

A. Yes. The fact that you are the author of the article will not save your patent application. The law provides that the inventor is not entitled to a patent if the invention has been described in a printed publication anywhere in the world more than a year before his patent application is filed.

Who May Obtain a Patent

15. *Q. Is there any restriction as to persons who may obtain a United States patent?*

    A. No. Any inventor may obtain a patent regardless of age or sex, by complying with the provisions of the law. A foreign citizen may obtain a patent under exactly the same conditions as a United States citizen.

16. *Q. If two or more persons work together to make an invention, to whom will the patent be granted?*

    A. If each had a share in the ideas forming the invention, they are joint inventors and a patent will be issued to them jointly on the basis of a proper patent application filed by them jointly. If on the other hand one of these persons has provided all of the ideas of the invention, and the other has only followed instructions in making it, the person who contributed the ideas is the sole inventor and the patent application and patent should be in his name alone.

17. *Q. If one person furnishes all of the ideas to make an invention and another employs him or furnishes the money for building and testing the invention, should the patent application be filed by them jointly?*

    A. No. The appliction must be signed, sworn to, and filed in the Patent Office, in the name of the true inventor. This is the person who furnishes the ideas, not the employer or the person who furnishes the money.

18. *Q. May a patent be granted if an inventor dies before filing his application?*

    A. Yes; the application may be filed by the inventor's executor or administrator.

19. *Q. While in England this summer, I found an article on sale which was very ingenious and has not been introduced into the United States or patented or described. May I obtain a United States patent on this invention?*

A. No. A United States patent may be obtained only by the true inventor, not by someone who learns of an invention of another.

Ownership and Sale of Patent Rights

20. *Q. May the inventor sell or otherwise transfer his right to his patent or patent application to someone else?*

A. Yes. He may sell all or any part of his interest in the patent application or patent to anyone by a properly worded assignment. The application must be filed in the Patent Office as the invention of the true inventor, however, and not as the invention of the person who has purchased the invention from him.

21. *Q. If two persons own a patent jointly, what can they do to grant a license to some third person or company to make, use or sell the invention?*

A. They may grant the license jointly, or either one of them may grant such a license without obtaining the consent of the other. A joint owner does not need to get the consent of his co-owner either to make, use, or sell the invention of the patent independently, or to grant licenses to others. This is true even though the joint owner who grants the license owns only a very small part of the patent. Unless you want to grant this power to a person to whom you assign a part interest, you should ask your lawyer to include special language in the assignment to prevent this result.

22. *Q. As joint inventor, I wish to protect myself against the possibility that my co-inventor may, without my approval, license some third party under our joint patent. How can I accomplish this?*

A. Consult your lawyer and ask him to prepare an agreement for execution by you and your co-inventor to protect each of you against this possibility.

Duration of Patents

23. *Q. For how long a term of years is a patent granted?*

A. Seventeen years from the date on which it is issued; except for patents on ornamental designs, which are granted for terms of 3½ , 7, or 14 years.

24. *Q. May the term of a patent be extended?*

A. Only by special act of Congress, and this occurs very rarely and only in most exceptional circumstances.

25. *Q. Does the patentee continue to have any control over use of the invention after his patent expires?*

A. No. Anyone has the free right to use an invention covered in an expired patent, so long as he does not use features covered in other unexpired patents in doing so.

Patent Searching

26. *Q. Where can a search be conducted?*

A. In the Search Room of the Patent Office in the Department of Commerce Building at 14th and E Streets N.W., Washington, D.C. Classified and numerically arranged sets of United States and foreign patents are kept there for public use.

27. *Q. Will the Patent Office make searches for individuals to help them decide whether to file patent applications?*

A. No. But it will assist inventors who come to Washington by helping them to find the proper patent classes in which to make their searches. In response to mail inquiries it will also advise inventors as to what patent classes and sub-classes to search. For a reasonable fee it will furnish lists of patents in any class and subclass, and copies of these patents may be purchased for 25 cents each.

Attorneys and Agents

28. *Q. Does the Patent Office control the fees charged by patent attorneys and agents for their services?*

A. No. This is a matter between you and your patent attorney or agent in which the Patent Office takes no part. In order to avoid possible misunderstanding you may wish to ask him for estimates in advance as to his approximate charges for: (a) the search, (b) preparation of the patent application, and (c) Patent Office prosecution.

29. *Q. Will the Patent Office inform me whether the patent attorney or agent I have selected is reliable or trustworthy?*

A. All patent attorneys and agents registered to practice before the Patent Office are expected to be reliable and trustworthy. The Patent Office can report only that a particular individual is, or is not, in good standing on the register.

30. *Q. If I am dissatisfied with my patent attorney or agent may I change to another?*

A. Yes, you can revoke your attorney's power of attorney any time you want to.

31. *Q. Will the Patent Office help me to select a patent attorney or agent to make my patent search or to prepare and prosecute my patent application?*

A. No. The Patent Office cannot make this choice for you, as it would be unfair for it to select some of its practitioners for recommendation as against others. However, your own friends or general attorney may help you in making a selection from among those listed as registered practitioners on the Patent Office roster.

32. *Q. How can I be sure that my patent attorney or agent will not reveal to others the secrets of my invention?*

A. Patent attorneys and agents earn their livelihood by the confidential services they perform for their clients, and if any attorney or agent improperly reveals an invention disclosed to him by a client, that attorney or agent is subject to disbarment from further practice before the Patent Office and loss of his livelihood. Persons who withhold information about their inventions from their attorneys and agents make a serious mistake, for the attorney or agent cannot do a fully effective job unless he is fully informed of every important detail.

Plant and Design Patents

33. *Q. Does the law provide patent protection for invention of new and ornamental designs for articles of manufacture, or for new varieties of plants?*

A. Yes. If you have made an invention in one of these fields, you should read the Patent Office pamphlet "General Information Concerning Patents."

Technical Knowledge Available From Patents

34. *Q. I have not made an invention but have encountered a problem. Can I obtain knowledge through patents of what has been done by others to solve the problem?*

A. The patents in the Patent Office Search Room in Washington contain a vast wealth of technical information and suggestions, organized in a manner which will enable you to review those most closely related to your field of interest. You may come to Washington and review these patents, or engage a patent practitioner to do this for you and to send you copies of the patents most closely related to your problem.

Infringement of Others' Patents

35. *Q. If I obtain a patent on my invention will that protect me against the claims of others who assert that I am infringing their patents when I make, use, or sell my own invention?*

A. No. There may be a patent of a more basic nature on which your invention is an improvement. If your invention is a detailed refinement or feature of such a basically protected invention, you may not use it without the consent of the patentee, just as no one will have the right to use your patented improvement without your consent. You should seek competent legal advice before starting to make or sell or use your invention commercially, even though it is protected by a patent granted to you.

Enforcement of Patent Rights

36. Q. Will the Patent Office help me to prosecute others if they infringe the rights granted to me by my patent?

A. No. The Patent Office has no jurisdiction over questions relating to the infringement of patent rights. If your patent is infringed you may sue the infringer in the appropriate United States court at your own expense.

Patent Protection in Foreign Countries

37. Q. Does a United States patent give protection in foreign countries?

A. No. The United States patent protects your invention only in this country. If you wish to protect your invention in foreign countries, you must file an application in the Patent Office of each such country within the time permitted by law. This may be quite expensive, both because of the cost of filing and prosecuting the individual patent applications, and because of the fact that most foreign countries require payment of taxes to maintain the patents in force. You should inquire of your practitioner about these costs before you decide to file in foreign countries.

Developing and Marketing Inventions and Patents

38. Q. Will the Patent Office advise me as to whether a certain patent promotion organization is reliable and trustworthy?

A. No. The Patent Office has no control over such organizations and cannot supply information about them. It is suggested that you obtain this information by inquiring of the Better Business Bureau of the city in which the organization is located, or of the Bureau of Commerce and Industry of the state in which the organization has its place of business. You may also undertake to make sure that you are dealing with reliable people by asking your own patent attorney or agent whether he has knowledge of them, or by inquiry of others who may know them.

39. *Q. Are there any organizations in my area which can tell me how and where I may be able to obtain assistance in developing and marketing my invention?*

A. Yes. In your own or neighboring communities you may inquire of such organizations as chambers of commerce, banks and area departments of power companies and railroads. Many communities have locally financed industrial development organizations which can help you locate manufacturers and individuals who might be interested in promoting your idea. You can also obtain assistance from one of the field offices of the U.S. Department of Commerce or of the Small Business Administration located near you.

40. *Q. Are there any state government agencies that can help me in developing and marketing my invention?*

A. Yes. In nearly all states there are state planning and development agencies or departments of commerce and industry that are seeking new product and new process ideas to assist manufacturers and communities in the state. If you do not know the names or addresses of your state organizations you can obtain this information by writing to the governor of your state.

41. *Q. Can the Patent Office assist me in the developing and marketing of my patent?*

A. Only to a very limited extent. The Patent Office cannot act or advise concerning the business transations or arrangements that are involved in the development and marketing of an invention. However, the Patent Office will publish, at the request of a patent owner, a notice in the "Official Gazette" that the patent is available for licensing or sale. The fee for this service is $3.

42. *Q. Can any U.S. Government agency other than the Patent Office assist me in the development and marketing of my invention?*

A. The Business and Defense Services Administration of the U.S. Department of Commerce, Washington, D.C., may be able to help you with information and advice, as its various industry divisions maintain close contact with all branches of American industry, or you may get in touch with one of the Department of Commerce field offices.

The Small Business Administration publishes monthly a products list circular containing brief descriptions of issued patents believed to be likely to interest prospective manufacturers, and these circulars are distributed to many business organizations. You may write a letter to the Small Business Administration, Washington, D.C., requesting that your invention be listed in this publication, and your request will be honored if the Small Business Administration decides that publication is desirable. The Small Business Administration has over 50 offices in various cities in the United States, and it offers through its products assistance program information and counsel to small concerns who are interested in new products. You may wish to get in touch with one of these offices of the Small Business Administration.

● libraries with files of patents (by number)

California
    Los Angeles   Public Library
Georgia
    Atlanta   Georgia Tech Library
Illinois
    Chicago   Main Branch, Public Library
Massachusetts
    Boston   Public Library
Michigan
    Detroit   Public Library
Minnesota
    Minneapolis   Public Library
Missouri
    Kansas City   Linda Hall Library
    St. Louis   Public Library
New Jersey
    Newark   Public Library
New York
    Albany   University of State of N. Y. Library
    Buffalo   Grosvenor Library
    New York   Public Library
Ohio
    Cincinnati   Public Library
    Cleveland   Public Library
    Columbus   Ohio State University Library
    Toledo   Public Library
Pennsylvania
    Philadelphia   Franklin Institute Library
    Pittsburgh   Carnegie Library
Rhode Island
    Providence   Public Library
Wisconsin
    Madison   Public Library
    Milwaukee   Public Library

● libraries with classified patent numbers (on microfilm)

The following list of libraries with microfilms of classified patent numbers was compiled late in 1961. It excludes libraries maintained by industrial corporations. There may be additions to the list from time to time.

ARKANSAS
Fayetteville—University of Arkansas Library

CALIFORNIA
Berkeley—University of California Library
Los Angeles—Public Library
University of California Library
Sacramento—Public Library
San Diego—Public Library
San Francisco—Public Library
Stockton—Public Library

COLORADO
Boulder—University of Colorado Library
Denver—Public Library

GEORGIA
Atlanta—Georgia Tech Library

ILLINOIS
Chicago—Public Library

INDIANA
Gary—Public Library
Indianapolis—Public Library
Lafayette—Purdue University Library

IOWA
Iowa City—State University of Iowa Library

LOUISIANA
New Orleans—Public Library

MASSACHUSETTS
Boston—Public Library
Lowell—Lowell Technological Institute Library
Worcester—Public Library

MICHIGAN
Ann Arbor—University of Michigan Library
Detroit—Public Library
University of Detroit Library

MINNESOTA
Minneapolis—Public Library
University of Minnesota Library
St. Paul—Public Library

MISSOURI
Kansas City—Linda Hall Library
Public Library
St. Louis—Public Library

NEW JERSEY
Newark—Public Library
Princeton—Princeton University Library

NEW YORK
Albany—University of the State of New York Library
Brooklyn—Public Library
Buffalo—Buffalo & Erie County Public Library
Jamaica—Public Library

NORTH CAROLINA
Chapel Hill—University of North Carolina Library
Durham—Duke University Library
Raleigh—North Carolina State College Library

OHIO
Akron—Public Library
Cincinnati—Public Library
Columbus—Ohio State University Library
Oxford—Miami University Library
Toledo—Public Library

OKLAHOMA
Oklahoma City—Public Library
Stillwater—Oklahoma A&M College Library

OREGON
Corvallis—Oregon State College Library
Salem—Public Library

PENNSYLVANIA
Philadelphia—Franklin Institute Library
            Public Library
Pittsburgh—Carnegie Library

SOUTH DAKOTA
Brookings—South Dakota State College of Agriculture and
            Mechanic Arts Library

TEXAS
Dallas—Public Library
Denton—North Texas State College Library
Fort Worth—Public Library
Lubbock—Texas Technological College Library

UTAH
Salt Lake City—University of Utah Library

WASHINGTON
Seattle—Public Library

WISCONSIN
Madison—State Historical Society of Wisconsin Library
Milwaukee—Public Library

● libraries receiving the official gazette

The following list of libraries that receive the *Official Gazette* was compiled from official records in 1961. Most of the institutions also receive the annual *Index of Patents* and many of them the loose-leaf *Classification Manual*.

As the distribution changes from time to time, it is well to ask the libraries near you which publications they currently have available.

ALABAMA
Auburn—Auburn Univerity Library
Birmingham—Public Library
Tuskegee Institute—Hollis Burke Frissell Library
Tuscaloosa—University of Alabama Library

ALASKA
College—University of Alaska Library

ARIZONA
Phoenix—Department of Library and Archives
Phoenix Public Library
Tempe—Arizona State University, Matthews Library
Tucson—Tucson Public Library
University of Arizona Library

ARKANSAS
Fayetteville—University of Arkansas Library
Little Rock—Little Rock Public Library

CALIFORNIA
Bakersfield—Kern County Free Library

158

Berkeley—University of California Library
Claremont—Pomona College, Honnold Library
Davis—University of California Library
Eureka—Eureka Free Library
Fresno—Fresno County Free Library
Long Beach—Public Library
Los Angeles—Los Angeles Public Library
         University of California at Los Angeles
         Library
         University of California, School of Law
         Library
         University of Southern California Library
Oakland—Oakland Public Library
Pasadena—Pasadena Public Library
Pomona—Los Angeles County Law Library
Redding—Shasta County Free Library
Redlands—University of Redlands Library
Richmond—Richmond Public Library
Riverside—Riverside Public Library
Sacramento—California State Library
         City Free Library
San Diego—San Diego County Law Library
         San Diego Public Library
San Francisco—Mechanics Mercantile Library
         San Francisco Law Library
         San Francisco Public Library
San Jose—San Jose Public Library
Santa Barbara—Santa Barbara Public Library
Stanford University—Stanford University Library
Stockton—Stockton Free Public Library

COLORADO
Boulder—University of Colorado Library
Colorado Springs—Colorado College, Coburn Library

Denver—Public Library
  Supreme Court Library
  University of Denver, Mary Reed Library
Fort Collins—Colorado State University Library
Golden—Colorado School of Mines Library
Pueblo—McClelland Public Library

CONNETICUT
Bridgeport—Bridgeport Public Library
Hartford—Connecticut State Library
  Hartford Public Library
Meriden—Curtis Memorial Library
Middletown—The Russell Library
  Wesleyan University, Olin Library
New Britain—Library of the New Britain Institute
New Haven—Free Public Library
  Yale University Library
Storrs—University of Connecticut Library
Waterbury—Silas Bronson Library

DELAWARE
Newark—University of Delaware Library
Wilmington—Wilmington Institute Free Library

DISTRICT OF COLUMBIA
Washington—Department of Agriculture Library
  Department of Interior Central Library
  Navy Department Library

FLORIDA
Coral Gables—University of Miami Library
Gainesville—University of Florida Library
Miami—Dade County Law Library
  Miami Public Library
New Smyrna Beach—Public Library
Tampa—University of Tampa Library

GEORGIA
Athens—University of Georgia General Library
Atlanta—Atlanta Public Library
    Georgia Institute of Technology Library
HAWAII
Honolulu—Library of Hawaii
    University of Hawaii Library
IDAHO
Boise—Idaho State Law Library
Moscow—University of Idaho Library
Pocatello—Idaho State College Library
ILLINOIS
Carbondale—Southern Illinois University Library
Chicago—Chicago Public Library
    John Crerar Library
    University of Chicago Libraries
    University of Illinois Library
Decatur—Decatur Public Library
Evanston—Northwestern University Library
Galesburg—Galesburg Public Library
Joliet—Public Library
Kankakee—Kankakee Public Library
Moline—Moline Public Library
Peoria—Peoria Public Library
Rock Island—Rock Island Public Library
Rockford—Public Library
Springfield—Illinois State Library
Urbana—Chicago Public Library
INDIANA
Bloomington—Indiana University Library
Evansville—Evansville Public Library
Fort Wayne—Indiana Tech. College Library
    Public Library

Gary—Gary Public Library
Hammond—Hammond Public Library
Indianapolis—Indiana State Library
      Indianapolis Public Library
Lafayette—Purdue University Library
Muncie—Public Library
Notre Dame—University of Notre Dame Library
Richmond—Morrison-Reeves Library

IOWA
Ames—Iowa State College Library
Des Moines—Iowa State Traveling Library
      State Law Library
      Public Library
Dubuque—Carnegie Stout Free Public Library
Iowa City—State University of Iowa Library
Sioux City—Public Library

KANSAS
Kansas City—Public Library
Lawrence—University of Kansas Library
Manhattan—Kansas City College Library
Topeka—Kansas State Library
Wichita—University of Wichita Library

KENTUCKY
Ashland—Ashland Public Library
Lexington—University of Kentucky Library
Louisville—Louisville Free Public Library
      University of Louisville Library
Newport—Newport Public Library
Pikeville—Pikeville College Library

LOUISIANA
Baton Rouge—Louisiana State University Library
Lafayette—Southwestern Louisiana Institute Library

Lake Charles—McNeese State College Library
New Orleans—Law Library of Louisiana
Louisiana State Museum Library
New Orleans Public Library
Tulane University, Howard-Tilton Memorial Library
Ruston—Louisiana Polytechnic Institute Library
Shreveport—Shreve Memorial Library

MAINE
Augusta—Maine State Library
Bangor—Bangor Public Library
Lewiston—Bates College Library
Lewiston Public Library
Orono—University of Maine Library
Portland—Portland Public Library
Portland University Law School Library

MARYLAND
Baltimore—Enoch Pratt Free Library
Johns Hopkins University Library
Bethesda—Bethesda–Chevy Chase High School Library
College Park—University of Maryland Library

MASSACHUSETTS
Amherst—University of Massachusetts, Goodell Library
Boston—Boston Public Library
Harvard Business School Library
Social Law Library
State Library of Massachusetts
Cambridge—Harvard College Library, Serials Division
Harvard Law School Library
Massachusetts Institute of Technology Library
Leominster Public Library

Lowell—Lowell City Library
      Lowell Textile Institute Library
Lynn—Lynn Public Library
New Bedford—Public Library
Newton—Newton City Library
Springfield—City Library Association
Tufts College—Tufts College Library
Worcester—Free Public Library

MICHIGAN

Ann Arbor—University of Michigan, General Library
Battle Creek—Willard Library
Bay City—Bay City Public Library
Benton Harbor—Benton Harbor Public Library
Detroit—Detroit Public Library
      Marygrove College Library
      University of Detroit Library
      Wayne State University Library
East Lansing—Michigan State College of Agriculture
      and Applied Science Library
Flint—The Public Library
Grand Rapids—Grand Rapids Bar Assn. Library
      Grand Rapids Public Library
Houghton—Michigan College of Mining and Technology Library
Jackson—Jackson Public Library
Kalamazoo—Public Library
Lansing—Michigan State Library
Muskegon—Hackley Public Library
Port Huron—The Port Huron Public Library
Saginaw—Hoyt Public Library

MINNESOTA

Duluth—Duluth Bar Association Library
      Duluth Public Library

Minneapolis—Business and Municipal Branch Library
    Public Library
    University of Minnesota Library
Northfield—St. Olaf College Library
St. Cloud—Public Library
St. Paul—Minnesota State Law Library
    St. Paul Public Library

MISSISSIPPI
Hattiesburg—Mississippi Southern College Library
Jackson—Mississippi State Library
Starkville—Mississippi State University, Mitchell Memorial
    Library
University—University of Mississippi Library

MISSOURI
Columbia—University of Missouri Library
Joplin—Joplin Public Library
Kansas City—Bar Association Library
    Kansas City Public Library
    University of Kansas City Library
Rolla—School of Mines and Metallurgy Library
St. Joseph—St. Joseph Public Library
St. Louis—St. Louis Public Library
    St. Louis University Library
    Washington University Library
Springfield—Drury College Library

MONTANA
Bozeman—Montana State College Library
Helena—Helena Public Library

NEBRASKA
Lincoln—Nebraska State Library
    University of Nebraska Library
Omaha—Omaha Public Library

NEVADA
Reno—University of Nevada Library

NEW HAMPSHIRE
Concord—New Hampshire State Library
Durham—University of New Hampshire Library
Laconia—Laconia Public Library

NEW JERSEY
Atlantic City—Free Public Library
Bayonne—Free Public Library
Camden—Camden County Bar Association Library
    Camden Free Public Library
Elizabeth—Public Library
Jersey City—Free Public Library
New Brunswick—Free Public Library
    Rutgers University Library
Newark—Public Library
Princeton—Princeton University Library
South Orange—Seton Hall University Library
Trenton—Free Public Library
    Rider College Library

NEW MEXICO
Albuquerque—University of New Mexico Library
Los Alamos—University of California Library
Santa Fe—New Mexico State Law Library
University Park—New Mexico State University

NEW YORK
Albany—New York State Library
Bay Shore—Bay Shore Public Library
Binghamton—Binghamton Public Library
Brooklyn—Brooklyn Public Library
    Brooklyn Technical High School Library
    Pratt Institute Library

Buffalo—Buffalo and Erie County Public Library
Elmhurst—Queens Borough Public Library
Farmingdale—Long Island Agricultural and Technical
Institute Library
Fordham University—Fordham University Library
Jamaica—Queens Borough Public Library
St. Johns University Library
New York City—College of the City of New York
Library
Columbia University Library
Cooper Union Library
New York Law Institute Library
New York Public Library (Forty-
second Street Branch)
New York University Library
Niagara Falls—Niagara Falls Public Library
Potsdam—Clarkson College of Technology Library
Rochester—Rochester Public Library, Edgerton Branch
University of Rochester Library
St. Bonaventure—St. Bonaventure College Library
Schenectady—Union College Library
Staten Island—Supreme Court Library
Syracuse—Syracuse Public Library
Syracuse University Library
Troy—Troy Public Library
Utica—Utica Public Library
White Plains—Supreme Court Law Library
Yonkers—Yonkers Public Library

NORTH CAROLINA
Asheville—The Pack Memorial Library
Chapel Hill—University of North Carolina Library
Charlotte—Charlotte Public Library
Durham—Duke University Library

Greensboro—Agricultural and Technical College Library
Raleigh—D. H. Hill Library of North Carolina State
  College
  North Carolina State Library
Winston-Salem—Public Library of Winston-Salem and
  Forsyth County
  Wake Forest College Library

NORTH DAKOTA
Fargo—North Dakota Agricultural College and Experi-
  mental Station Library
Grand Forks—University of North Dakota Library
Hansboro—Hansboro Public School Library
Wahpeton—North Dakota State School of Science
  Library

OHIO
Akron—Akron Public Library
Alliance—Mt. Union College Library
Ashland—Ashland College Library
Athens—Ohio University Library
Bowling Green—Bowling Green State University Library
  Public Library
Canton—Canton Public Library Association
Cincinnati—Public Library
  University of Cincinnati Library
Cleveland—Cleveland Public Library
  Fenn College Library
  Miles Park Branch Library
  Western Reserve University Library
Columbus—Battelle Memorial Institute Library
  Columbus Public Library
  Ohio State Library
  Ohio State University Library
Dayton—Dayton Public Library

Hamilton—Lane Public Library
Lima—Lima Public Library
Mansfield—Mansfield Public Library
Marietta—Marietta College Library
Oxford—Miami University Library
Springfield—Warder Public Library
　　　Wittenburg College Library
Toledo—Toledo Public Library
Warren—Warren Public Library
Youngstown—Youngstown Public Library

OKLAHOMA
Ada—East Central State Teachers College Library
Enid—Carnegie Public Library
Langston—Langston University Library
Norman—University of Oklahoma Library
Oklahoma City—Oklahoma City Library
　　　Oklahoma State Library
Okmulgee—Okmulgee Public Library
Stillwater—Oklahoma State University Library
Tahlequah—Northeastern State Teachers College Library
Tulsa—Tulsa Public Library
　　　University of Tulsa Library

OREGON
Ashland—Southern Oregon College of Education Library
Eugene—University of Oregon Library
Forest Grove—Pacific University Library
Portland—Multnomah County Law Library
Salem—Oregon State Library

PENNSYLVANIA
Allentown—Allentown Free Library
　　　Muhlenberg College Library
Beaver Falls—Carnegie Library
Bethlehem—Lehigh University Library

Bradford—Carnegie Public Library
Chester—J. Lewis Crozer Library
Easton—LaFayette College Library
Erie—Erie Public Library
Gettysburg—Gettysburg College Library
Harrisburg—Pennsylvania State Library
Lancaster—Franklin and Marshall College, Fackenthal
    Library
Oil City—Oil City Public Library
Philadelphia—Drexel Institute Library
    Free Library of Philadelphia
    Messlein Library
    Philadelphia Bar Assn. Law Library
    Temple University Law Library
Pittsburgh—Allegheny Regional Branch Library
    Carnegie Library of Pittsburgh
    Mellon Institute Library
    University of Pittsburgh Library
    West End Carnegie Library
Reading—Reading Public Library
Scranton—Scranton Public Library
State College—Pennsylvania State University Library
Warren—Warren Library Association
Washington—Memorial Library of Washington and
    Jefferson College
Wilkes-Barre—Kings College Library
    Osterhout Free Library
Williamsport—James V. Brown Library
    Williamsport Technical Institute Library

PUERTO RICO
Mayaguez—University of Puerto Rico, College of Agricul-
    ture and Mechanical Arts Library
Río Piedras—University of Puerto Rico General Library

RHODE ISLAND
Kingston—University of Rhode Island Library
Pawtucket—Deborah Cook Sayles Public Library
Providence—Providence Public Library
      Rhode Island State Library
Westerly—Westerly Public Library

SOUTH CAROLINA
Clemson—Clemson College Library
Columbia—University of South Carolina Library

SOUTH DAKOTA
Brookings—South Dakota State College Lincoln Memo-
      rial Library
Rapid City—Free public Library
Vermillion—University of South Dakota Library

TENNESSEE
Chattanooga—Chattanooga Public Library
Cookeville—Tennessee Polytechnic Institute Library
Jackson—Jackson Free Library
Johnson City—East Tennessee State College Library
Knoxville—University of Tennessee Library
Memphis—Cossitt Library
      The Goodwyn Institute Library
Nashville—Joint University Libraries
      State Library Division, Tennessee State
      Library and Archives
      State Library Division, Tennessee State
      Library and Archives

TEXAS
Abilene—Hardin Simmons University Library
Amarillo—Potter County Free Library
Austin—Texas State Library
      University of Texas Library

Beaumont—Lamar State College of Technology Library
College Station—Agriculture and Mechanical College of
      Texas Library
Dallas—Dallas Public Library
      Southern Methodist University Library
Denton—North Texas State College Library
Edinburg—Pan American College Library
El Paso—El Paso Public Library
Fort Worth—Fort Worth Public Library
      Texas Christian University Library
Galveston—Rosenberg Library
Houston—Houston Public Library
Kingsville—Texas College of Arts and Industries Library
Lubbock—Texas Technological College Library
Marshall—Bishop College Library
San Antonio—Public Library, Business and Science De-
      partment
      Southwest Research Institute Library
Waco—Baylor University Library

UTAH

Logan—Utah State University of Agriculture and Applied
      Science Library
Ogden—Carnegie Free Library
Provo—Brigham Young University Library
Salt Lake City—University of Utah Library

VERMONT

Northfield—Norwich University Library

VIRGINIA

Appomattox—County Library
Blacksburg—Virginia Polytechnic Institute Library
Danville—Danville Public Library
Emory—Emory and Henry College Library

Lexington—Virginia Military Institute Library
Norfolk—Norfolk Public Library
Richmond—Richmond Public Library
          Virginia State Library
Roanoke—Roanoke Public Library
Charlottesville—University of Virginia Library

WASHINGTON
Hoquiam—Hoquiam Public Library
Olympia—Washington State Library
Pullman—State College of Washington Library
Seattle—Seattle Public Library
        Seattle University Library
        University of Washington Library
Spokane—Spokane Public Library
Tacoma—Tacoma Public Library
Walla Walla—Whitman College Library

WEST VIRGINIA
Athens—Concord College Library
Beckley—Beckley Public Library
Huntington—Marshall College Library
Institute—West Virgina State College Library
Morgantown—West Virginia University Library

WISCONSIN
Appleton—Lawrence College Library
Beloit—Beloit College Library
Green Bay—Kellogg Public Library
Janesville—Janesville Public Library
LaCrosse—Public Library
Madison—State Historical Society Library
        University of Wisconsin Library
Milwaukee—Milwaukee Public Library
Oshkosh—Oshkosh State College Library
        Oshkosh Public Library

Racine—Racine Public Library
Stevens Point—Wisconsin State College Library
Wausau—Wausau Public Library

WYOMING

Casper—Natrona County Public Library
Cheyenne—Wyoming State Library
Laramie—University of Wyoming Library

• patent office fees and payments

1. Filing fee. On filing each original application for a patent
   having 20 claims or less, except in design cases---------- $30.00
   For each additional claim over 20------------------------ 1.00
2. Final fee. On issuing each original patent having 20 claims
   or less, except in design cases-------------------------- 30.00
   For each additional claim over 20------------------------ 1.00
3. Filing fee, designs. In design cases:
   For term of 3 years and 6 months----------------------- 10.00
   For term of 7 years----------------------------------- 15.00
   For term of 14 years---------------------------------- 30.00
4. Filing fee, reissues. On every application for the reissue of
   a patent-- 30.00
   For each claim which is in excess of 20 as well as in excess
   of the number of claims in the original patent----------- 1.00
5. On filing each petition for the revival of an abandoned application for patent--------------------------------------- 10.00
6. On filing each petition for the delayed payment of the
   final fee-- 10.00
7. On an appeal for the first time from the primary examiner to
   the Board of Appeals------------------------------------ 25.00
8. On filing each disclaimer------------------------------- 10.00
9. For certification of copies of records, etc., in any case, in
   addition to the cost of copy certified------------------ 1.00
10. For certificate of correction of applicant's mistake-------- 10.00
11. For uncertified printed copies of the specifications and ac-
    companying drawings of patents, except design patents,
    if in print, each-------------------------------------- .25
12. For uncertified printed copies of design patents, if in print-- .10
13. For recording every assignment, agreement, or other paper,
    not exceeding six pages-------------------------------- 3.00
    For each additional patent or application included or in-
    volved in one writing, where more than one is so included
    or involved, additional-------------------------------- .50
    For each additional two pages or less------------------ 1.00
14. For typewritten copies of records, for each page produced
    (double-spaced) or fraction thereof-------------------- 1.00
15. For photocopies or other reproductions of records, drawings
    or printed material, per page of material copied--------- .30

16. For abstracts of title to each patent or application:
For the search, one hour or less, and certificate-------------- 3.00
Each additional hour or fraction thereof-------------------- 1.50
For each brief from the digest of assignments, of 200 words
or less--- 1.00
Each additional 100 words or fraction thereof-------------- .10
17. For translations from foreign languages into English, made
only of references cited in applications or of papers filed
in the Patent Office insofar as facilities may be available:
Written translations, for every 100 words of the original language, or fraction thereof------------------------------ 3.00
Oral translations (dictation or assistance), for each one-half
hour or fraction thereof that service is rendered---------- 4.00
18. For making patent drawings, when facilities are available,
the cost of making the same, minimum charge per sheet-- 25.00
19. For correcting drawings, the cost of making the correction,
minimum charge--- 3.00
20. For the mounting of unmounted drawings and photoprints
received with patent applications, provided they are of
approved permanency------------------------------------- 1.00
21. Lists of U.S. Patents:
All patents in a subclass, per sheet (containing 100 patent
numbers or less)--- .30
Patents in a subclass limited by date or patent number,
per sheet (containing 50 numbers or less)-------------- .30
22. Search of Patent Office records for purposes not otherwise
specified in this section, per hour of search or fraction
thereof-- 3.00
23. For special service to expedite furnishing items or services
ahead of regular order:
On orders for copies of U.S. patents and trademark reg-
istrations, in addition to the charge for the copies, for
each copy ordered--------------------------------------- .25
On all other orders or requests for which special service
facilities are available, in addition to the regular charge, a
special service charge equal to the amount of regular
charge; minimum special service charge per order or
request-- 1.00
24. For air mail delivery:
On "special service" orders to destinations to which U.S.
domestic air mail postage rates apply, no additional
charge.
On regular service orders to any destination and "special
service" orders to destinations other than those specified
in the preceding subparagraph, an additional charge
equal to the amount of air mail postage. (Available only

when the ordering party has, with the Patent Office, a deposit account.)

25. For items and services, that the Commissioner finds may be supplied, for which fees are not specified by statute or by this section, such charges as may be determined by the Commissioner with respect to each such item or service.

● patent office requirements for drawings

A drawing is required by the statute in all cases which admit of drawings. This includes practically all inventions except compositions of matter or processes, but a drawing may also be useful in the case of many processes.

The drawing may be signed by the inventor himself or it may be signed by the attorney or agent for the inventor (but note that the signature to the written part of the application must be that of the inventor himself and cannot be signed by anyone else).

The drawing must show every feature of the invention specified in the claims and is required by the Office rules to be in a particular form. The Office specifies the size of the sheet on which the drawing is made, the type of paper, the margins, and other details relating to the making of the drawing. The reason for specifying the standards in detail is that the drawings are printed and published in a uniform style when the patent issues, and the drawings must also be such that they can be readily understood by persons using the patent descriptions.

The following is the rule relating to the standards for drawings:

84. *Standards for drawings.*—The complete drawing is printed and published when the patent issues, and a copy is attached to the patent. This work is done by the photolithographic process, the sheets of drawings being reduced about one-third in size. In addition, a reduction of a selected portion of the drawings of each application is published in the Official Gazette. It is therefore necessary for these and other reasons that the character of each drawing be brought as nearly as possible to a uniform standard of execution and excellence, suited to the requirements of the reproduction process and of the use of the drawings, to give the best results in the interests of inventors, of the Office, and of the public. The following regulations with respect to drawings are accordingly prescribed:

(*a*) *Paper and ink.*—Drawings must be made upon pure white paper of a thickness corresponding to two-ply or three-ply Bristol board. The surface of the paper must be calendared and smooth and of a quality which will permit erasure and correction. India ink alone must be used for pen drawings to secure perfectly black solid lines. The use of white pigment to cover lines is not acceptable.

(*b*) *Size of sheet and margins.*—The size of a sheet on which a drawing is made must be exactly 10 by 15 inches. One inch from its edges a single marginal line is to be drawn, leaving the "sight" precisely 8 by 13 inches. Within this margin all work must be included. One of the shorter sides of the sheet is regarded as its top, and, measuring down from the marginal line, a space of not less than 1¼ inches is to be left blank for the heading of title, name, number, and date, which will be applied subsequently by the Office in a uniform style.

(c) *Character of lines.*—All drawings must be made with drafting instruments or by photolithographic process which will give them satisfactory reproduction characteristics. Every line and letter (signatures included) must be absolutely black. This direction applies to all lines however fine, to shading, and to lines representing cut surfaces in sectional views. All lines must be clean, sharp, and solid, and fine or crowded lines should be avoided. Solid black should not be used for sectional or surface shading. Freehand work should be avoided wherever it is possible to do so.

(d) *Hatching and shading.*—Hatching should be made by oblique parallel lines, which may be not less than about one-twentieth inch apart.

Heavy lines on the shade side of objects should be used except where they tend to thicken the work and obscure reference characters. The light should come from the upper left-hand corner at an angle of 45°. Surface delineations should be shown by proper shading, which should be open.

(e) *Scale.*—The scale to which a drawing is made ought to be large enough to show the mechanism without crowding when the drawing is reduced in reproduction, and views of portions of the mechanism on a larger scale should be used when necessary to show details clearly; two or more sheets should be used if one does not give sufficient room to accomplish this end, but the number of sheets should not be more than is necessary.

(f) *Reference characters.*—The different views should be consecutively numbered figures. Reference numerals (and letters, but numerals are preferred) must be plain, legible, and carefully formed, and not be encircled. They should, if possible, measure at least one-eighth of an inch in height so that they may bear reduction to one twenty-fourth of an inch; and they may be slightly larger when there is sufficient room. They must not be so placed in the close and complex parts of the drawing as to interfere with a thorough comprehension of the same, and therefore should rarely cross or mingle with the lines. When necessarily grouped around a certain part, they should be placed at a little distance, at the closest point where there is available space, and connected by lines with the parts to which they refer. They should not be placed upon hatched or shaded surfaces but when necessary, a blank space may be left in the hatching or shading where the character occurs so that it shall appear perfectly distinct and separate from the work. The same part of an invention appearing in more than one view of the drawing must always be designated by the same character, and the same character must never be used to designate different parts.

(g) *Symbols, legends.*—Graphical drawing symbols for conventional elements may be used when appropriate, subject to approval by the Office. The elements for which such symbols are used must be adequately identified in the specification. While descriptive matter on drawings is not permitted, suitable legends may be used, or may be required, in proper cases, as in diagrammatic views and flow sheets or to show materials. Arrows may be required, in proper cases, to show direction of movement. The lettering should be as large as, or larger than, the reference characters.

(h) *Location of signature and names.*—The signature of the applicant or the name of the applicant and signature of the attorney or agent, may be placed in the lower right-hand corner of each sheet within the marginal line, or may be placed below the lower marginal line.

(i) *Views.*—The drawing must contain as many figures as may be necessary to show the invention; the figures should be consecutively numbered if possible, in the order in which they appear. The figures may be plan, elevation, section, or perspective views, and detail views of portions or elements, on a larger scale if necessary may also be used. Exploded views, with the separated parts of the same figure embraced by a bracket, to show the relationship or order of assembly of various parts are permissible. When necessary, a view of a large machine or device in its entirety may be broken and extended over several sheets if there is no loss in facility of understanding the view (the different parts should be identified by the same figure number but followed by the letters a, b, c, etc., for each part). The plane upon which a sectional view is taken should be indicated on the general view by a broken line, the ends of which should be designated by numerals corresponding to the figure number of the sectional view and have arrows applied to indicate the direction in which the view is taken. A moved position may be shown by a broken line superimposed upon a suitable figure if this can be done without crowding, otherwise a separate figure must be used for this purpose. Modified forms of construction can only be shown in separate figures. Views should not be connected by projection lines nor should center lines be used.

(j) *Arrangement of views.*—All views on the same sheet must stand in the same direction and should, if possible, stand so that they can be read with the sheet held in an upright position. If views longer than the width of the sheet are necessary for the clearest illustration of the invention, the sheet may be turned on its side. The space for a heading must then be reserved at the right and the signatures placed at the left, occupying the same space and position on the sheet as in the upright views and being horizontal when the sheet is held in an upright position. One figure must not be placed upon another or within the outline of another.

(k) *Figure for Official Gazette.*—The drawing should, as far as possible, be so planned that one of the views will be suitable for publication in the Official Gazette as the illustration of the invention.

(l) *Extraneous matter.*—An agent's or attorney's stamp, or address, or other extraneous matter, will not be permitted upon the face of a drawing, within or without the marginal line, except that the title of the invention and identifying indicia, to distinguish from other drawings filed at the same time, may be placed below the lower margin.

(m) *Transmission of drawings.*—Drawings, transmitted to the Office should be sent flat, protected by a sheet of heavy binder's board, or may be rolled for transmission in a suitable mailing tube; but must never be folded. If received creased or mutilated, new drawings will be required.

The requirements relating to drawings are strictly enforced, but a drawing not complying with all of the regulations is accepted for purpose of examination, and correction or a new drawing will be required later.

• basic patent office forms

1. PATENT APPLICATION, SOLE INVENTOR; PETITION, POWER OF ATTORNEY, OATH

To the Commissioner of Patents:

Your petitioner, ----------------------, a citizen of the United States and a resident of -------------------, State of -------------------, whose post-office address is -------------------, prays that letters patent may be granted to him for the improvement in -------------------, set forth in the following specification; and he hereby appoints -------------------, of -------------------, (Registration No. ----------), his attorney (or agent) to prosecute this application and to transact all business in the Patent Office connected therewith. (If no power of attorney is to be included in the application, omit the appointment of the attorney.)

[The specification, which includes the description of the invention and the claims, is written here.]

-------------------, the above-named petitioner, being sworn (or affirmed), deposes and says that he is a citizen of the United States and resident of --------------------, State of -------------------, that he verily believes himself to be the original, first, and sole inventor of the improvement in -------------------- described and claimed in the foregoing specification; that he does not know and does not believe that the same was ever known or used before his invention thereof, or patented or described in any printed publication in any country before his invention thereof, or more than one year prior to this application, or in public use or on sale in the United States for more than one year prior to this application; that said invention has not been patented in any country foreign to the United States on an application filed by him or his legal representatives or assigns more than twelve months prior to this application; and that no application for patent on said invention has been filed by him or his representatives or assigns in any country foreign to the United States, except as follows --------------------.

(Inventor's full signature)

State of --------------- }
County of --------------- } ss:

Sworn to and subscribed before me this ------ day of -------------------, 19---.

[SEAL]

(Signature of notary or officer)

(Official character)

182

2. PATENT APPLICATION, JOINT INVENTORS; PETITION, POWER OF ATTORNEY, OATH

To THE COMMISSIONER OF PATENTS:

Your petitioners, -------------------- and --------------------, citizens of the United States and residents, respectively, of ----------------------, State of --------------------, and of --------------------, State of --------- ----------, whose post-office addresses are, respectively, ------------------ and -------------------- pray that letters patent may be granted to them, as joint inventors, for the improvement in --------------------, set forth in the following specification; and they hereby appoint -------------------- of -------------------- (Registration No. --------), their attorney (or agent), to prosecute this application and to transact all business in the Patent Office connected therewith. (If no power of attorney is to be included in the application, omit the appointment of the attorney.)

[The specification, which includes the description of the invention and the claims, is written here.]

---------------------- and ----------------------, the above-named petitioners, being sworn (or affirmed), depose and say that they are citizens of the United States, and residents of ----------------------, State of --------------------, that they verily believe themselves to be the original, first and joint inventors of the improvement in -------------------- described and claimed in the foregoing specification; that they do not know and do not believe that the same was ever known or used before their invention thereof, or patented or described in any printed publication in any country before their invention thereof, or more than one year prior to this application, or in public use or on sale in the United States for more than one year prior to this application; that said invention has not been patented in any country foreign to the United States on an application filed by them or their legal representatives or assigns more than 12 months prior to this application; and that no application for patent on said invention has been filed by them or their representatives or assigns in any country foreign to the United States, except as follows: ------------------ --

----

(Inventors' full signatures)

STATE OF ----------------- }
County of --------------- } ss:
Sworn to and subscribed before me this ------ day of ------------------, 19---.

(Signature of notary or officer)

[SEAL]   --
(Official character)

3. PATENT APPLICATION, ADMINISTRATOR OF DECEASED INVENTOR; PETITION, POWER OF ATTORNEY, OATH

To the Commissioner of Patents:

Your petitioner, A _____ B _____, a citizen of the United States and a resident of _____, State of _____, whose post-office address is _____, administrator of the estate of C _____ D _____, late a citizen of the United States and a resident of _____, State of _____, deceased (as by reference to the duly certified copy of letters of administration, hereto annexed, will more fully appear), prays that letters patent may be granted to him for the invention of the said C _____ D _____ for an improvement in _____, set forth in the following specification; and he hereby appoints _____, of _____ (Registration No. _____), his attorney (or agent), to prosecute this application and to transact all business in the Patent Office connected therewith.

(If no power of attorney is to be included in the application, omit the appointment of the attorney.)

[The specification, which includes the description of the invention and the claims, is written here.]

A _____ B _____, the above-named petitioner, being sworn (or affirmed), deposes and says that he is a citizen of the United States of America and a resident of _____, that he is the administrator of the estate (or executor of the last will and testament) of C _____ D _____, deceased, late a citizen of the United States and resident of _____, that he verily believes the said C _____ D _____ to be the original, first and sole inventor of the improvement in _____ described and claimed in the foregoing specification; that he does not know and does not believe that the same was ever known or used before the invention thereof by the said C _____ D _____, or patented or described in any printed publication in any country before the said invention thereof, or more than one year prior to this application, or in public use or on sale in the United States for more than one year prior to this application; that said invention has not been patented in any country foreign to the United States on an application filed by the said C _____ D _____ or his legal representatives or assigns more than 12 months prior to this application; and that no application for patent on said invention has been filed by the said C _____ D _____ or his representatives or assigns in any country foreign to the United States, except as follows: _____

A _____ B _____

(Signature)

ADMINISTRATOR, ETC.

STATE OF ---------------- ⎱ ss:
County of -------------- ⎰
Sworn to and subscribed before me this ------ day of ------------------,
19---.
[SEAL]   ------------------------------------
                            (Signature of notary or officer)

                            (Official character)

4. OATH NOT ACCOMPANYING APPLICATION

STATE OF ---------------- ⎱ ss:
County of -------------- ⎰
----------------------, being sworn (or affirmed, deposes and says that
he is a citizen of the United States of America and resident of
--------------------, that on --------------------, 19---, he filed application for patent Serial No. ------------ in the United States Patent Office,
that he verily believes himself to be the original, first and sole inventor of
the improvement in -------------------- described and claimed in the
specification of said application for patent; that he does not know and does
not believe that the same was ever known or used before his invention
thereof, or patented or described in any printed publication in any country
before his invention thereof, or more than one year prior to the date of
said application, or in public use or on sale in the United States for more
than one year prior to the date of said application; that said invention has
not been patented before the date of said application in any country
foreign to the United States on an application filed by him or his legal
representatives or assigns more than twelve months prior to the date of
said application; and that no application for patent on said invention has
been filed by him or his representatives or assigns in any country foreign
to the United States, except as follows: --------------------------------.

                            (Inventor's full signature)
Sworn to and subscribed before me this ------ day of ------------------,
19---.
                            (Signature of notary or officer)
[SEAL]   ------------------------------------
                            (Officer character)

5. DESIGN APPLICATION

To THE COMMISSIONER OF PATENTS:

Your petitioner, --------------------, a citizen of the United States and a resident of -------------------- in the county of -------------------- and State of ------------------, whose post-office address is ------------------, city of --------------------, State of --------------------, prays that letters patent may be granted to him for the term of 3½ years (or 7 years or 14 years) for the new and original design for --------------------, set forth in the following specification; and he hereby appoints, --------------------, of ---------------------, (Registration No. --------), his attorney (or agent), to prosecute this application and to transact all business in the Patent Office connected therewith.

Be it known that I have invented a new, original, and ornamental design for -------------------- of which the following is a specification, reference being had to the accompanying drawing, forming a part hereof.

The figure is a plan view of a --------------------, showing my new design.

I claim:

The ornamental design for a --------------------, as shown.

--------------------, the above-named petitioner being sworn (or affirmed), deposes and says that he is a citizen of the United States and resident of county of --------------------, State of --------------------, that he verily believes himself to be the original, first, and sole inventor of the design for -------------------- described and claimed in the foregoing specification; that he does not know and does not believe that the same was ever known or used before his invention thereof, or patented or described in any printed publication in any country before his invention thereof, or more than one year prior to this application, or in public use or on sale in the United States for more than one year prior to this application; that said design has not been patented in any country foreign to the United States on an application filed by him or his legal representatives or assigns more than 6 months prior to this application; and that no application for patent on said design has been filed by him or his representatives or assigns in any country foreign to the United States, except as follows: --

----
(Inventor's full signature)

STATE OF ---------------- ⎱
County of -------------- ⎰ ss:

Sworn to and subscribed before me this ------ day of ------------------, 19---.

(Signature of notary or officer)

[SEAL]

(Official character)

6. PLANT PATENT APPLICATION; PETITION, POWER OF ATTORNEY, OATH

To THE COMMISSIONER OF PATENTS:

Your petitioner, --------------------, a citizen of the United States and a resident of ---------------------, in the State of ---------------------, whose post-office address is --------------------, prays that letters patent may be granted to him for the new and distinct variety of --------------, set forth in the following specification; and he hereby appoints ---------- --------------, of ------------------ (Registration No. --------), his attorney (or agent), to prosecute this application and to transact all business in the Patent Office connected therewith.

(If no power of attorney is to be included in the application, omit the appointment of the attorney.)

[The specification, which includes the description of the invention and the claims, is written here.]

---------------------, the above-named petitioner, being sworn (or affirmed), deposes and says that he is a citizen of the United States of America and resident of --------------------, that he verily believes himself to be the original, first, and sole inventor of the new and distinct variety of ---------------------- described and claimed in the foregoing specification; that he has asexually reproduced the said new and distinct variety; that he does not know and does not believe that the same was ever known or used before his invention thereof, or patented or described in any printed publication in any country before his invention thereof, or more than one year prior to this application, or in public use or on sale in the United States for more than one year prior to this application; that said invention has not been patented in any country foreign to the United States on an application filed by him or his legal representatives or assigns more than 12 months prior to this application; and that no application for patent on said new and distinct variety or plant has been filed by him or his representatives or assigns in any country foreign to the United States, except as follows: ----------------------------

----
(Inventor's full signature)

STATE OF --------------- } ss:
County of --------------- }
Sworn to and subscribed before me this ------ day of ------------------, 19---.

(Signature of notary or officer)

[SEAL]

(Official character)

7. POWER OF ATTORNEY OR AUTHORIZATION OF AGENT, NOT ACCOMPANYING APPLICATION

To THE COMMISSIONER OF PATENTS:

The undersigned having, on or about the _____ day of _____, 19___, made application for letters patent for an improvement in _____ _____, Serial Number _____, hereby appoints _____ of _____, State of _____, Registration No. _____, his attorney (or agent), to prosecute said application, and to transact all business in the Patent Office connected therewith.

———————————————————————————————
(Signature)

8. REVOCATION OF POWER ATTORNEY OR AUTHORIZATION OF AGENT

To THE COMMISSIONERS OF PATENTS:

The undersigned having, on or about the _____ day of _____, 19___, appointed _____, of _____, State of _____, his attorney (or agent) to prosecute an application for letters patent which application was filed on or about the _____ day of _____, 19___, for an improvement in _____, Serial Number _____, hereby revokes the power of attorney (or authorization of agent) then given.

———————————————————————————————
(Signature)

9. ASSIGNMENT OF PATENT

(No special form is prescribed for assignments, which may contain various provisions depending upon the agreement of the parties. The following two forms are specimens of assignments which have been used in some cases.)

WHEREAS, I, _____, of _____, did obtain Letters Patent of the United States for an improvement in _____ No. _____, dated _____; and whereas, I am now the sole owner of said patent; and,

WHEREAS, _____, of _____, whose post-office address is _____, City of _____, and State of _____, is desirous of acquiring the entire interest in the same;

Now, THEREFORE, in consideration of the sum of _____ dollars ($_____), the receipt of which is hereby acknowledged, and other good and valuable considerations, I, _____, by these presents do sell, assign, and transfer unto the said --------------------, the entire right, title, and interest in and to the said Letters Patent aforesaid; the same to be held and enjoyed by the said --------------------, for his own use and behoof, and for his legal representatives and assigns, to the full end of the term for which said Letters Patent are granted, as fully and entirely as the same would have been held by me had his assignment and sale not been made.

Executed, this ------- day of --------------, 19---, at ------------------.

STATE OF --------------- ⎫ *ss:*
County of -------------- ⎭
Before me personally appeared said ----------------- and acknowledged the foregoing instrument to be his free act and deed this ------- day of ----------------, 19---.

(Notary Public)

[SEAL]

10. ASSIGNMENT OF APPLICATION

WHEREAS, I, --------------------, of -------------------- have invented certain new and useful Improvements in ----------------------, for which an application for United States Letters Patent was filed on -------------- ---------------, Serial No. --------, [if the application has been prepared but not yet filed, state "for which an application for United States Letters Patent was executed on --------------------," instead] and

WHEREAS, --------------------, of --------------------, whose post-office address is --------------------, is desirous of acquiring the entire right, title and interest in the same;

Now, THEREFORE, in consideration of the sum of ------------ dollars ($----------), the receipt whereof is hereby acknowledged, and other good and valuable consideration, I, the said --------------------, by these presents do sell, assign and transfer unto said --------------------, the full and exclusive right to the said invention in the United States and the entire right, title, and interest in and to any and all Letters Patent which may be granted, therefore in the United States.

I hereby authorize and request the Commissioner of Patents to issue Letters Patent to said --------------------, as the assignee of the entire right, title, and interest in and to the same, for his sole use and behoof; and for the use and behoof of his legal representatives, to the full end of the term for which said Letters Patent may be granted, as fully and entirely as the same would have been held by me had this assignment and sale not been made.

Executed this ------- day of --------------, 19 ---, at --------------------.

STATE OF -------------- $\Big\}$ *ss:*
County of --------------

Before me personally appeared said -------------------- and acknowledged the foregoing instrument to be his free act and deed this -------
day of ----------------, 19----.

[SEAL]   ------------------------------------
                              (Notary Public)

• company requirements for consideration of outside inventions: sample statement of policy

Most large companies have substantially the same requirements concerning the consideration of inventions and "ideas." The following excerpt from a booklet issued by one large firm is presented as typical. It differs only in detail and wording from the requirements of other concerns:

The _____ Company has a large staff of engineers and technicians devoted to improving its products and methods. In a tradition established through more than a half century, this staff is constantly working on the development of both new and old ideas. In addition to its own original work it has access to a large number of prior patents, prior publications, and other sources of information. It is not surprising, therefore, that many of the ideas submitted to the Company by outsiders are already known or available to it through the efforts of this staff. We feel sure that it will be accepted as only reasonable that compensation will not be given for the duplication of such old or previously available ideas should the Company at any time elect to practice them, whether or not we have previously given specific consideration to such ideas.

The Company sincerely desires that every person protect himself to his own satisfaction before disclosing an idea to it. At the same time, we must also protect our interests so that we can conduct an efficient and progressive business.

The Company has therefore adopted the following policies concerning submitted ideas, which it hopes will receive your sympathetic understanding:

A. All ideas should be submitted in writing. (If, after a written description of an idea has been submitted, a personal interview seems desirable, it may be arranged with certainty that the proper persons will be present. In view of the fact that Company employees are located in various cities, this cannot be done without full information as to the subject matter to be considered.)

B. Where ideas are received which appear to have been submitted gratuitously (without expectation of compensation), written confirmation of the writer's intention will nevertheless be requested to avoid misunderstanding. (The form printed on page 11 of this booklet may be used to indicate that the idea is submitted gratuitiously.)

C. The Company is unwilling to consider any idea on the condition that, prior to its disclosure, an agreement to be consummated setting forth some basis of compensation for its use. (Experience shows that even the most sincerely offered "pig-in-a-poke" cannot be adequately appraised without inspection.)

D. No consideration will be given to any **idea submitted in the expectation of compensation** unless it is submitted subject to the **CONDITIONS OF SUBMISSION** which are set forth and explained below. The submitter, if his idea is to receive consideration, must agree to these Conditions by filling out and returning to the Submitted Ideas Office the detachable form entitled "Acceptance of Conditions," which constitutes page 15 of this booklet.

1. **No confidential relationship is to be established by such submission or implied from consideration of the submitted material, and the material is not to be considered to be submitted "in confidence."** (Confidential relationships have been held to create obligations which are beyond those that the Company is willing to assume.)

2. **The Company makes no commitment that the idea or material submitted in connection with it shall be kept a secret.** (It is often necessary to refer the submission to a number of different persons in the _____ Company and its affiliated companies to ascertain whether or not it is of interest. The organization is a large one and continually changing. Thus, while there may be no intention of giving it any publicity, its secrecy cannot be promised.)

3. **The Company does not agree to pay any compensation whatsoever for its use of ideas which have not been patented. If, despite the conditions herein contained to the contrary, it shall be alleged that the Company has incurred liability to the submitter with respect to any unpatented idea submitted to it, the submitter agrees that in no event shall he assert any claim for equitable relief or for damages in excess of $1,000, which**

sum the submitter agrees shall be the maximum damages for any and all liability of the Company with respect to such unpatented idea, including but not limited to the Company's use or disclosure thereof. If any such unpatented idea shall subsequently be covered by the claims of a patent, the foregoing clause shall not apply to any rights under such patent. (Business ideas—and many technical ideas which have been known to others or which relate to minor changes in products and manufacturing techniques—are unpatentable. The Company can rarely compensate for such ideas, even though used by it, because they can be freely copied by competitors as soon as put into use. If the prospective submitter of such an idea expects compensation for it, the Company advises him not to submit it. If an idea is submitted which, though presently unpatented, appears to be validly patentable, we may, if interested, negotiate for the acquisition of patent rights that may later be protected by a patent. Regardless of our action, the submitter should be guided by his attorney as to the desirability of seeking a patent on his idea.)

4. The reception and consideration by the Company of any submitted disclosure of an idea shall not in any way impair the Company's right to contest the validity or infringement of any patent that may have been or may thereafter be obtained on it. The submitter's sole remedy if he believes the Company to be infringing such patent shall be enforcement by him under the applicable patent laws of such exclusive rights as he may possess by virtue of his patent. (We receive many ideas which we know or believe to be old. Some of these nevertheless subsequently become the subject of patents which are inadvertently granted by the Patent Office because of its failure to discover earlier publications or uses of the same subject matter which, if considered, would have prevented the grant of a patent. The Company must obviously retain its freedom to contest the validity or infringement of such patents, and, in particular, desires to be in no worse position in this regard than parties who have not had dealings with the patentee.)

5. The Company will give each submitted idea only such consideration as in the judgment of the Company it merits. (Because of the fact that a very large number of submitted ideas must be handled, we cannot accept any obligation to give any item special handling or to refer it to specified individuals or Company officers.)

6. The Company shall be under no obligation to return any material submitted or to reveal its acts in connection with the submitted idea. (It is necessary that we be permitted to keep such material so that reference may be made to it if a question should arise as to just what was disclosed. The person submitting it should therefore keep a duplicate for his own record.)

7. The Company shall be under no obligation to reveal any information regarding its activities in either the general or specific field to which the submitted idea pertains. (The Company is continuously active in many fields and at all times has many new developments in process. While in some cases it has no objection to advising submitters of work which it has done or is doing, it would obviously be unfair that mere receipt of a submitted idea should place it under obligation to disclose its confidential activities in related fields.)

8. If the Company decides not to offer compensation for a submitted idea, it assumes no obligation to give reasons for its decision—or to do other than to communicate its decision to the submitter. (In some cases—as where the particular proposal has been made many times before—we can readily state the facts and will endeavor to do this where the conditions warrant. In other cases, a statement of reasons cannot be given without disclosing confidential information or going into greater detail than would be practical.)

9. Entering into negotiations for the purchase of any idea submitted, or the making of any offer for its purchase, shall not in any way prejudice the Company, nor shall it be deemed an admission of the novelty of the idea, or of priority or originality on the part of the person submitting it or of any other person.

10. Any and all prior negotiations or agreements by any agent or representative of the Company are merged into these Conditions of Submission and no such prior representations, negotiations or agreements shall be binding on the Company or of any force or effect.

11. The foregoing Conditions may not be modified or waived except in writing signed by an officer of the Company, the General Manager of a Division of the Company, or the Company's General Patent Counsel.

• sample agreement of contract
between inventor and manufacturer

In drawing an agreement licensing the manufacture and sale of an invention, the attorney will prepare a contract to fit the situation. The specimen reproduced here contains standard provisions, and is one that is commonly used. It is intended as a sample only, to give the inventor some idea of what to expect in such an agreement.

No inventor should attempt to draw such a legal instrument himself, but should rely on his attorney or broker.

THIS AGREEMENT, made this _____ day of _____, 19___, by and between _____, and hereinafter referred to as "Inventor"; and _____ _____, and hereinafter referred to as "Licensee."

WHEREAS, Inventor represents and warrants that he is sole owner of all right, title and interest in, to and under United States Letters Patent No. _____, issued _____, on a device entitled _____; and

WHEREAS, Licensee is desirous of acquiring an exclusive license to manufacture, use and sell said devices under said Letters Patent, upon the terms and conditions hereinafter set forth:

NOW THEREFORE, the said parties hereto in consideration of the mutual covenants and agreements contained herein, and in further consideration of the sum of $_____, receipt of which is hereby acknowledged, the parties hereto do hereby agree as follows:

1. Inventor hereby grants to Licensee the sole and exclusive license to manufacture, use and sell in all foreign and domestic markets the said devices and throughout life of this agreement on the terms and conditions hereinafter stated. The life of this agreement shall be the same as the life of the patents, unless sooner terminated as hereinafter provided.

2. Licensee agrees to pay Inventor a royalty of _____ of Licensee's billed price on each and every said device sold, said

royalty to be due and payable at the end of each three-month period. Royalties accruing each three-month period shall be payable not later than the 25th of the month following the end of the period.

3. Licensee shall at all times keep true and correct records of accounts showing the total number of said devices sold and these accounts shall be open to inspection by Inventor or his duly appointed agent or auditor at all and proper times, and Licensee shall render a full statement of net sales made at the end of each three-month period.

4. Licensee shall affix or cause to be affixed to each of said devices, or to the box or container in which said devices may be packaged, the inscription "Patent No. _____."

5. If at any time hereafter, during the continuance of this agreement, Inventor shall make any improvement in said device, then such improvement shall inure to the benefit of Licensee without any addition to the royalty percentage stipulated herein. Conversely, any improvement to said device made by Licensee shall inure to the benefit of Inventor under terms and royalty payments set forth hereinbefore.

6. In event that said Letters Patents should be infringed upon, then Licensee may at its election prosecute such infringement at its own expense and retain any monies awarded in settlement. However, if Licensee elects not to prosecute, then Inventor may if he so elects, do so at his expense and retain any monies awarded in settlement.

7. In the event said Letters Patent should be claimed to be infringing another patent, then Licensee and Inventor shall defend jointly and shall share equally in the costs. If Inventor is unable financially to advance his share of the costs, then Licensee may withhold royalty payments during the pendency of any such action until accrued royalties equal Inventor's share of said costs.

8. If, in the event of any such suit or suits, the said Letters Patents should be found invalid or found to be infringing the rights of another Letters Patent, then Licensee shall have the right to terminate this agreement.

9. Licensee shall have the right to grant sub-licenses to other manufacturers under the same terms and conditions and royalty payments to Inventor as is granted in this agreement.

10. It is recognized by both parties hereto that Licensee will require a certain length of time to work out production and sales problems and therefore no minimum requirements shall be effective between the date of this Agreement and the 1st day of _____.

However, Licensee agrees to expedite production and sales as much as possible and to pay royalty as provided herein on all said devices sold during this period. In subsequent years, beginning with _____, Licensee agrees to pay to Inventor the following scale of minimum royalties:

(A) In the first year, _____, through _____, royalty shall be paid on sales of a minimum of _____ said devices.

(B) In the second year, _____, through _____, royalty shall be paid on sales of a minimum of _____ said devices.

(C) Beginning with the year _____, and all subsequent years for the life of this agreement, royalty shall be paid on sales of a minimum of _____ said devices each year.

Failure of Licensee to pay this stated minimum annual royalty shall give Inventor the right to terminate this agreement at his option.

11. Licensee further agrees that it will diligently pursue the manufacture and sale of said devices during the life of this agreement and will exert its best efforts toward creating a demand therefor.

12. Licensee agrees that it will not, during the term of this agreement, directly or indirectly attack or question the validity of any Letters Patent owned by Inventor in connection with said subject device.

13. It is agreed that if royalties, or any part thereof shall at any time be in arrears after the same shall become due, or if Licensee shall become bankrupt, or insolvent, or enter into any composition with its creditors, or shall make any default in performing any of the agreements contained herein, then it shall be lawful for the Inventor, by written notice by registered mail to Licensee's last known address, to revoke this license, which shall thereupon become void, without prejudice to any right of action or remedy of the Inventor for the recovery of any monies then due the Inventor hereunder. Inventor shall, in the event of any breach of any provisions of this agreement, notify Licensee in writing, by registered mail, to Licensee's last known address, and Licensee shall have 30 days in which to comply or correct any such breach of the provisions.

14. This Agreement may be terminated at any time by the mutual consent of both parties, or by Licensee by giving 30 days written notice to Inventor at his last known address. In the event of such

termination, Licensee shall pay over the full amount of the royalties then owing Inventor.

15. This Agreement shall not be transferable by Licensee except by the written consent of Inventor, and shall be binding upon the heirs, assigns or personal representatives of the Inventor.

IN WITNESS WHEREOF the Inventor has hereunto subscribed his name, and Licensee has caused this agreement to be executed in its corporate name, by its proper officer thereunto duly authorized, and its corporate seal to be hereto affixed, as of this day and year first above written.

In Presence of: INVENTOR:

_____   _____

_____

In Presence of:
(Or Corporate Seal)

_____   LICENSEE:

_____   By: _____ Title:_____

● typical contract for assignment
of invention to employer

In consideration of my employment in any capacity with the
_____ Company and of the salary or wages paid for
my services in the course of such employment, I agree

(A) to communicate to the Company promptly and fully all inventions made or conceived by me (whether made solely by me or jointly with others) from the time of entering the Company's employ until I leave, (1) which are along the lines of the business, work or investigations of the Company or of companies which it owns or controls at the time of such inventions, or (2) which result from or are suggested by any work which I may do for or on behalf of the Company;

(B) to assist the Company and its nominees during and subsequent to such employment in every proper way (entirely at its or their expense) to obtain for its or their own benefit patents for such inventions in any and all countries, said inventions to be and remain the sole and exclusive property of the Company or its nominees whether patented or not;

(C) to make and maintain adequate and current written records of all such inventions, in the form of notes, sketches, drawings, or reports relating thereto, which records shall be and remain the property of and available to the Company at all times;

(D) except as the Company may otherwise consent in writing, not to disclose at any time (except as my Company duties may require) either during or subsequent to my employment, any information, knowledge, or data of the Company I may receive or develop during the course of my employment, relating to formulas, business processes, methods, machines, manufactures, compositions, inventions, discoveries or other matters which are of a secret* or confidential* nature;

(E) to notify the Company in writing before I make any disclosure or perform or cause to be performed any work for or on behalf of the Company, which appears to threaten conflict with (1) rights I claim in any invention or idea (a) conceived by me or others prior to my employment or (b) otherwise outside the scope of this agreement, or (2) rights of others arising out of obligations incurred by me (a) prior to this agreement or (b) otherwise outside the scope of this agreement. In the event of my failure to give notice under the circumstances specified in (1) of the foregoing, the Company may assume that no such conflicting invention or idea exists, and I agree that I will make no claim against the Company with respect to the use of any such invention or idea in any work or the product of any work which I perform or cause to be performed for or on behalf of the Company.

This agreement may not on behalf of or in respect to the Company be changed or modified, or released, discharged, abandoned or otherwise terminated, in whole or in part, except by an instrument in writing signed by an officer or other authorized executive of the Company.

This agreement shall be binding upon my heirs, executors, administrators or other legal representatives or assigns.

I represent that except as stated on the reverse of this agreement I have no agreements with or obligations to others in conflict with the foregoing.

These terms are used in the ordinary sense and do not refer to official security classifications of the United States Government.

● small business administration field offices

Alabama:
    Birmingham—2030 First Avenue N.

Alaska:
    Anchorage—307 Penthouse

Arizona:
    Phoenix—2727 North Central Avenue

Arkansas:
    Little Rock—600 W. Capitol Avenue

California:
    Los Angeles—312 W. Fifth Street
    San Francisco—525 Market Street

Colorado:
    Denver—909 17th Street

Connecticut:
    Hartford—450 Main Street

District of Columbia:
    Washington, D.C.—726 Jackson Place N.W.

Florida:
    Jacksonville—47 W. Forsyth Street
    Miami—168 S.E. First Street

Georgia:
    Atlanta—90 Fairlie Street, N.W.

Hawaii:
    Honolulu—195 S. King Street

Idaho:
    Boise—910 Main Street

Illinois:
    Chicago—219 S. Clark Street

Indiana:
    Indianapolis—130 E. Washington Street

Iowa:
Des Moines—5th Street and Grand Avenue

Kansas:
Wichita—120 S. Market Street

Kentucky:
Louisville—4th and Broadway

Louisiana:
New Orleans—610 South Street

Maine:
Augusta—114 Western Avenue

Maryland:
Baltimore—Fayette and St. Paul Streets

Massachusetts:
Boston—407 Atlantic Avenue

Michigan:
Detroit—232 W. Grand River Avenue

Minnesota:
Minneapolis—603 2nd Avenue S.

Mississippi:
Jackson—Capitol and West Streets

Missouri:
Kansas City—1006 Grand Avenue
St. Louis—1520 Market Street

Montana:
Helena—Main Street and Sixth Avenue

Nebraska:
Omaha—215 N. 17th Street

New Hampshire:
Concord—72 N. Main Street

New Mexico:
Albuquerque—5th and Gold Streets, S.W.

New York:
Buffalo—295 Main Street
New York—42 Broadway
Syracuse—500 S. Salina Street

North Carolina:
Charlotte—201 S. Tryon Street

North Dakota:
    Fargo—207 N. Fifth Street

Ohio:
    Cleveland—1370 Ontario Street
    Columbus—50 W. Day Street

Oklahoma:
    Oklahoma City—3rd and Robinson Streets

Oregon:
    Portland—921 S.W. Washington

Pennsylvania:
    Philadelphia—1015 Chestnut Street
    Pittsburgh—107 Sixth Street

Puerto Rico:
    Santurce—1200 Ponce de Leon Avenue

Rhode Island:
    Providence—57 Eddy Street

South Carolina:
    Columbia—1801 Assembly Street

South Dakota:
    Sioux Falls—109½ N. Main Avenue

Tennessee:
    Knoxville—301 W. Cumberland Avenue
    Nashville—500 Union Street

Texas:
    Dallas—1025 Elm Street
    Houston—515 Rusk Avenue
    Lubbock—240 Federal Office Building
    Marshall—101 E. Austin Street
    San Antonio—434 S. Main Avenue

Utah:
    Salt Lake City—136 S. Main Street

Vermont:
    Montpelier—79 Main Street

Virgin Islands:
    St. Thomas—P.O. Box 1242

Virginia:
    Richmond—1904 Byrd Avenue

Washington:
  Seattle—506 2nd Avenue
  Spokane—W. 940 Riverside
West Virgina:
  Charleston—500 Quarrier Street
  Clarksburg—227 W. Pike Street
Wisconsin:
  Madison—114 N. Carroll Street

● publications of the patent office

The following publications can be purchased from, and money orders should be made payable to, the Superintendent of Documents, Washington, D.C. (except where otherwise noted). When no price is given, the indication is that the price varies. It may be obtained from the Patent Office.

Official Gazette of the United States Patent Office—The *Official Gazette* is the official journal relating to patents and trademarks. It is issued each Tuesday, simultaneously with the weekly issue of the patents. It contains a claim and a selected figure of the drawings of each patent granted on that day; decisions in patent and trademark cases rendered by the courts and the Patent Office; notices of patent and trademark suits; indexes of patents and patentees; list of patents available for license or sale; and much general information such as orders, notices, changes in rules, changes in classification, etc. Annual subscription, $30.00; single copies, 75¢.

Index of Patents—This annual index to the *Official Gazette* contains an alphabetical index of the names of patentees and a list identifying the subject matter of the patents granted during the calendar year. At present it is issued in two volumes, one for patents and one for trademarks.

Decisions of the Commissioner of Patents—This is an annual volume republishing the decisions which have been published weekly in the *Official Gazette*.

Manual of Classification—This is a loose-leaf book containing a list of all the classes and subclasses of inventions in the Patent Office classification of patents, a subject matter index, and other information relating to classification. Substitute pages are issued from time to time. $8.50.

Classification Bulletins—The various changes and advances in classification made from time to time are collected and published

205

in bulletins which give these changes and the definitions of new and revised classes and subclasses.

Patent Laws—A compilation of the patent laws in force is issued, and revised editions are published from time to time. 30¢.

Trademark Laws—A compilation of the trademark laws in force is issued, and revised editions are published from time to time. 20¢.

Rules of Practice of the United States Patent Office in Patent Cases —This publication contains the rules governing the procedures in the Patent Office which have been adopted by the Commissioner under the authority of the patent statutes and approved by the Secretary of Commerce, and supplementary material, including forms and relevant sections of the patent law. 45¢.

Trademark Rules of Practice of the United States Patent Office— This contains the rules governing the procedure in the Patent Office in trademark matters. 30¢.

General Information Concerning Patents—This pamphlet is designed for the layman and contains a large amount of general information concerning the granting of patents expressed in non-technical language. Single copies may be obtained free from the Commissoner of Patents.

General Information Concerning Trademarks—This pamphlet serves the same purpose with reference to trademarks as the preceding does concerning patents. Single copies may be obtained free from the Commissioner of Patents.

Patents and Inventions, an Information Aid for Inventors—The purpose of this pamphlet is to help inventors in deciding whether to apply for patents, in obtaining patent protection, and in promoting their inventions. 15¢.

Roster of Attorneys and Agents Registered to Practice Before The United States Patent Office—This list of registered attorneys and agents is arranged alphabetically and by States and cities. $1.00.

Patent Attorneys and Agents Available to Represent Inventors Before the United States Patent Office—This pamphlet lists only those patent attorneys and agents registered to prepare and prosecute patent applications before the Patent Office who are available to represent individual inventors and companies. Attorneys and agents who are not available to represent individual inventors and companies because they are employed by a corporate employer or by the U.S. Government are not listed. 45¢.

Manual of Patent Examining Procedure—This manual is written for examiners in the Patent Office and gives in great detail the procedures followed by the examiners. $4.00. Foreign, $5.00.

Guide for Patent Draftsmen—A statement of Patent Office requirements for patent drawings, with illustrations. 15¢.

● selected bibliography of periodical literature: articles helpful to independent inventors

"Brokers Who Deal in Ideas; Inventions Find Their Way to Market through Help of New Product Scouts." *Business Week;* p. 99–100+; Sept. 26, '59.
"Building Profits on Outside Inventions." G. S. Hastings. *Dun's Review and Modern Industry;* 71:43–4+; June, '58.
"Champions for Radical New Inventions" (problem of significant technological innovation in business and military). D. A. Schon. *Harvard Business Review;* 41:77–86; Mar. '63.
"Checklist; Inventions that Baffle Uncle Sam." *Product Engineering;* 28: 117; Nov. 11, '57.
"City Asks Inventors to Help It Diversify" (Los Angeles Chamber of Commerce stages idea show). *Business Week;* p. 84–6; Apr. 2, '60.
"Defense Idea Requirements." *Aviation Week;* 70:31; May 25, '59.
"Developing your Inventing Ability." E. Randsepp. *Popular Mechanics;* 117:100–1; June, '62.
"Discoveries and Patentable Inventions." A. W. Gray. Bibliog. *Audio;* 44:46+; Oct., '60.
"Economics of Inventions; A Survey of the Literature." R. R. Nelson. Bibliog. *Journal of Business;* 32:101–27; Apr., '59.
"Electronics Genius." *Ebony;* 17:54+; Sept., '62.
"Employee-Inventor Gets his Cut." *Business Week;* p. 133–4; March 23, '63.
"Everybody Is an Inventor." J. C. Green. *Popular Mechanics;* 110: 102–3+; Sept., '58; Same abbreviated with title, "Let's Put Our Inventive Talent to Work." *Reader's Digest;* 73:209–11; Sept., '58.
"Exploiting your Idea." *Science News Letter;* 82:42–3; July 21, '62.
"Financing Inventions; from Banks and Insurers." *Economist;* 202: 152; Jan. 13, '62.
"Financing Inventions; Getting Started." *Economist;* 206:1142; March 23, '63.
"Financing Inventions; Risky Business." *Economist;* 206:447; Feb. 2, '63.
"Future Unlimited." C. F. Kettering. *Saturday Evening Post;* 230: 44–5+; May 17, '58.

"Have Invention, Need Angel." *Life;* 44:101–2; May 12, '58.
"How Does the Government Treat the Independent Inventor."
J. C. Green. *Product Engineering;* 31:55; Aug. 15, '60.
"How Does the Patent System Affect You; Contracts/Agreements
Vary." D. R. Stemple, jr. *Chemical Engineering Progress;* 59:11–
12; July, '63.
"How One Inventor Put his Product on the Market." (Pre-fab fiber-
glass marine float). *Industrial Marketing;* 45:140; Oct., '60.
"How to Cash in on your Invention." N. Carlisle. *Popular Science;*
183:122–4+; Oct., '63.
"How to Invent." F. E. Gilmore. *Petroleum Refiner;* 37:187–9+
Aug.; 396:400 Sept.; 196–8+ Oct.; 334–5 Nov.; 175–8+ Dec.; '58;
38:316–7+ Jan.; 203–6 Feb., '59.
"Individual Invention, A Lost Art?" W. J. Kroll. *Product Engineer-
ing;* 29:32–3; Feb. 24, '58.
"Invention; Vital Third Dimension of Science"; editorial. W. J.
Sparks. *Industrial and Engineering Chemical Product Research
and Development;* 3:1–2; March, '64.
"Invention and Enterprise." T. I. Williams. *Chemistry & Industry;*
p. 2085–8; Dec. 23, '61.
"Invention and Insight." R. E. Mueller. *Institute of Radio Engineer-
ing Procedure;* 46:783; April, '58.
"Invention Right of Employees." R. H. West, Jr. *Advanced Manage-
ment;* 26:17–18; Nov., '61.
"Inventions and Patents." A. H. Seidel. Bibliog. *Metal Finishing;*
57:51–4; March, '59.
"Inventions Anyone?" *Chemical & Engineering News;* 35:45–6;
Dec. 16, '57.
"Inventions Profit in Byproducts." *Product Engineering;* 35:41;
March 2, '64.
"Inventors Are Not Eggheads." G. X. Sand. *Popular Mechanics;*
112:97–101+; Oct., '59.
"Inventor's Code of Conduct." *Coal Age;* 69:122+; Feb., '64.
"Inventor's Inventor." S. T. Williamson. *Coronet;* 50: 168–71; July,
'61.
"Invisible Roadblocks to Invention." H. R. Johnson. *Product Engi-
neering;* 29:34–5; Feb. 10, '58.
"Just a Few Words Started Someone Thinking." B. Leerburger.
Electrical Merchandise Weekly; 94:51; Sept. 10, '62.
"Lead Inventors Get Cash." *Steel;* 143:49; Aug. 18, '58.
"Legally Acceptable Invention Records." G. M. Naimark. Bibliog.
Drug & Cosmetic Industry; 82:596–7+; May, '58.

"Techniques for Preparing a Patent",
Hrand M. Muheryan, Howard W
Sams & Co Inc., c 1973

"Lone Invention, No Lost Art." J. W. Lincoln. *Product Engineering;* 29:26–7; June 2, '58.

"Lone-wolf Inventor Still Holds his Own." *Saturday Evening Post;* 232:10; Sept. '59.

"Military Seeks Design." *Product Engineering;* 35:41; March 2, '64.

"Most Needed Inventions Listed by Armed Forces." *Machine Design;* 32:36+; Jan. 7, '60.

"Most Wanted Inventions." *Science Digest;* 46:93; Aug., '59.

"Most Wanted Inventions." *Science News Letter;* 75:343; May 30, '59.

"NASA Issues New Regulations on Space Act Patent Waivers." C. Lewis. *Aviation Week;* 71:39; Nov. 16, '59.

"Now Inventing Is Easier than Ever." N. Carlisle. *Popular Science;* 182:72–4+; May, '63.

"Open Doors to Serendipity." W. F. Thompson. *Industrial Laboratory;* 9:43–5; March, '58.

"Patent Utility." A. W. Gray. Bibliog. *Machine Design;* 31:150–3; March 19, '59.

"Patentee Profiles Aid Shell Recruiting (of researchers)." *Chemical Week;* 86:51+; June 4, '60.

"Patents and Inventive Effort." F. Machlup. Bibliog. *Science;* 133: 1463–6; May 12, '61; *Discussion,* 134:637+; Sept. 8, '61.

"Power of Concept." M. H. Parks. Bibliog. *Journal of Petroleum Technology;* 11:11–15; July, '59.

"Proper Word Isn't Creativity; It's Innovation We Want." D. E. Saffard. *Product Engineering;* 34:112–13; Dec. 9, '63.

"Proud Win for a Man with a Will." *Life;* 52:53+; May 11, '62.

"Rewards for Invention." *Product Engineering;* 34:60–3; April 29, '63.

"Role of Invention in Organized Society." E. H. Land. *Product Engineering;* 35:60–2; March 2, '64.

"Rules Followed by the Courts in Evaluating the Quality of an Invention." A. W. Gray. Bibliog. *Machine Design;* 31:106–10; Oct. 1, '59.

"Services Want Inventions." *Electronics;* 33:39; Jan. 22, '60.

"Should You Use Outside Inventors?" G. S. Hastings. *Product Engineering;* 29:29–30; Jan. 13, '58.

"Simultaneous Invention." *Science News Letter;* 77:374; June 11, '60.

"Stifling the One Human Asset." W. J. Coughlin. *Missiles & Rockets;* 10:46; Jan. 8, '62.

"Straight Talk to Inventors." M. Mann. *Popular Science;* 178: 122–4+; Feb.; 178: 112–15, March; 115–17+, April, '61.

"Successful Sucker." *Newsweek;* 57:84; May 22, '61.

"Tax Court Brightens Capital Gains Possibilities for Employee-Inventors." H. Oelbaum. *Journal of Taxation;* 19:306–7; Nov., '63.

"This Man is a Daf-fy Inventor." D. Scott. *Popular Science;* 179:51–3; July, '61.

"U.S. Inventors Respond to Armed Forces Ad." *Science News Letter;* 73:88; Feb. 8, '58.

"View from the Outside; What Royalties Should an Outside Inventor Get from a Company?" T. B. Holliday. *Product Engineering;* 34:62–3; Apr. 29, '63.

"Wanted: Inventions." F. V. Long, *Gas;* 35:131–2; Dec., '59.

"Wanted: Inventions." *Instruments and Automation;* 31:1524–5; Sept., '58.

"What to Make Out of This Junk?" *Life;* 53:45+; July 13, '62.

"What Will Happen to your Good Ideas?" R. Davis. *Engineering;* 196:388–9; Sept. 27, '63.

"What's Wanted." *Newsweek;* 53:83; June 1, '59.

"Where Are our Edisons (or for that matter, our Marconis and da Vincis)?" F. V. Long. *Gas;* 40:123+; Mar., '64; continued, 83+; Apr., '64.

"Where Are the Tinkerers?" *Time;* 80:81; Sept. 21, '62.

"Who Are the Innovators: (Prestige of Research Institutions Must not Overshadow Contributions of Individual Inventor)." *Economist;* 186:596–8; Feb. 15, '58.

"Who Owns Inventions?" *Nation's Business;* 48:14+; Feb., '60.

"Who Owns Your Employees Inventions?" (steps to avoid disputes). *Management Methods;* 14:64–6; May, '58.

"Why Can't a Man Invent More Like a Woman?" I. Chase. *Vogue;* 136:24+; Aug. 15, '60.

"Why Don't You Invent It?" P. Brock. *Popular Mechanics;* 113:84+; Feb., '60.

"Why Inventing is Still a One-Man Job." L. A. Williams. *Popular Science;* 179:70–2+; Sept., '61.

• selected bibliography of books helpful to independent inventors

Berle, Alf K., and L. Sprague de Camp. *Inventions, Patents and Their Management*. 1959. $15.00. Van Nostrand.

Burlingame, Roger, *March of the Iron Men*. 1960. paper, $2.25. Grosset & Dunlap (Universal Library).

Chayka, Louis. *Inventing for Profit*. $3.00. Humphries.

Clarke, Arthur C. *Profiles of the Future*. $3.95. Harper.

Cossman, E. Joseph. *How I Made $1,000,000 in Mail Order*. 1963. $5.95. Prentice-Hall.

De Camp, L. Sprague. *Heroic Age of American Invention*. 1961. $4.50. Doubleday.

Fanning, Leonard. *Fathers of Industries*. 1962. $4.75. Lippincott.

Field, Ernest. *How to Make Money in Your Own Business*. $12.50. 1965. Prentice-Hall.

Hadamard, Jacques. *Psychology of Invention in the Mathematical Field*. 1954. paper, $1.25. Dover.

Heath, Monroe. *Inventors and Scientists*. paper, $1.00. Pacific Coast.

Higgins, Frank V. *Inventing to Sell*. 1958. $5.00. Varsity.

Higgins, Frank V. *One Hundred and One Don'ts for Inventors*. 1957. paper, $4.00. Varsity.

Jewkes, John, and others. *Sources of Invention*. 1958. $6.75; paper, $4.25. St. Martin's Press.

Jones, Stacy. *You Ought to Patent That*. 1961. $4.00. Dial.

Leithäuser, Joachim G. *Inventor's Progress*. 1959. $4.50. World.

Liebers, Arthur. *Inventor's Complete Guide Book*. 1959. $1.00. Ottenheimer.

212

Mueller, Robert E. *Inventivity: How Man Creates in Art and Science.* 1963. $4.00. John Day.

Ries, Estelle H. *How to Get Ideas.* 1961. $3.00. G. S. Rand.

Rowland, John. *Epics of Invention.* 1957. $295. Dufour.

Thompson, Holland. *Age of Invention.* $3.95. U.S. Pubs.

Usher, Abbott P. *History of Mechanical Inventions.* Rev. ed. 1954. $9.75. Harvard.

Usher, A. P. *History of Mechanical Inventions.* 1959. paper $2.25. Beacon.

Woodling, George V. *Inventions and Their Protection.* 2nd ed. 1955. $10.00. Boardman, Clark.

Yates, Raymond F. *3100 Needed Inventions.* $3.50. Wilfred Funk.

Yates, Raymond F. *Yates' Guide to Successful Inventing.* $2.95. Wilfred Funk.

Yost, Edna. *Modern Americans in Science and Technology.* $3.25. Dodd Mead.

Index

index